Animal Facts
and Fallacies

Animal Facts
and Fallacies

By

Osmond P. Breland, Ph.D.

Associate Professor of Zoology
The University of Texas

with decorations by
Leo Hershfield

HARPER & ROW, *Publishers*
New York and Evanston

ANIMAL FACTS AND FALLACIES

To Nell

who has been most patient

Table of Contents

Contents

Contents

Contents

[x]

Contents

Part III: FISH

Contents

Contents

Contents

Preface

THERE has long been a demand for a nontechnical book about animals which considers such questions as these: can toads live for years in solid rock; what is the largest animal that ever lived; can the horned toad squirt blood from its eyes; will sharks attack human beings; are lizards poisonous; what is the largest fish; could a whale have swallowed Jonah; what is the difference between crocodiles and alligators?

So far as I know, there has previously been no one book that satisfactorily considers even the few questions listed above, and there are few people who know the correct answers. Yet, children and students are constantly asking questions of this kind. Indeed, such questions frequently occur even to curious adults. When one considers how difficult it is to find a nontechnical discussion of the unusual features of animals, it is not surprising that so many superstitious and incorrect beliefs are prevalent. Since information on these subjects is scattered throughout biological literature, which is not available to most people, it has seemed worth while to assemble the material into a single volume.

[xv]

Preface

This book would not have been possible without the wholehearted co-operation of persons connected with many institutions and organizations. These men and women, many of whom are authorities in their fields, have given freely of their time to answer questions concerning various animals: several have read parts of the manuscript and offered valuable suggestions. The writer wishes it were possible to name everyone who has been of help, but such a list would require many pages. The assistance of these friends is sincerely appreciated.

Let us now see how a few terms are used in the book. Many people use the term *animal* only for mammals, the group that includes such familiar forms as dogs, cats, horses, lions, elephants and other similar creatures. Actually, however, the word has a much broader meaning, as reference to any standard dictionary will show. Living things are divided into two large groups, the plant kingdom and the animal kingdom, and all creatures included within the animal kingdom may be called animals whether they are fish, birds, snakes, amphibians or mammals.

The present volume deals only with those animals that are vertebrates. This name indicates simply that the animal has a backbone, although all animals so classified do have many additional features in common. The backbone is divided into a number of parts or segments, and each segment is called a vertebra. Hence the use of the term *vertebrate* animal.

Some animals are said to be cold blooded, while others are warm blooded. These two names have nothing to do with the emotions of the creatures concerned, nor should they be taken too literally. They are used to describe the

Preface

presence or absence of a mechanism that regulates body temperatures. Cold-blooded animals are those that do not have much control of their own body temperatures, which change with the temperature of the environment. In warm weather, a cold-blooded animal may actually have a very high body temperature, which is the reason that the term is misleading if interpreted literally. Warm-blooded animals have a heat-regulating mechanism that keeps the body temperature constant, within narrow limits, despite changes in the outside temperature. Birds and mammals are the only vertebrate animals that are warm blooded; all the others are cold blooded.

Despite all precautions, there is always the possibility that errors will occur in a book such as this, or that important publications will have been overlooked. Many sources have been consulted, and great care has been exerted to verify all the statements included, but no pretense is made that every publication dealing with subjects in the text has been read. This could not be accomplished within a single lifetime. The author will sincerely appreciate having any errors or important omissions called to his attention.

Osmond P. Breland

Animal Facts *and* Fallacies

PART ONE
Mammals

What Are Mammals?

Mammals have a large number of features that are not present in other species. Two of these distinguishing characteristics are the presence of hair, and the possession by the female of structures called mammary glands which secrete milk for the young. These two features are fairly obvious in most mammals, especially in the familiar domestic species such as cows, horses, dogs and cats. The hair is clearly apparent; the mammary glands, well represented by the udder and teats of the cow, are also easily discovered in the females of most species. Even the sleek-skinned whales and other supposedly hairless mammals either have the hair represented by bristles about the mouth or possess hair during their younger stages.

Mammals are warm blooded: their body temperature remains relatively constant despite the variation of the outside temperature. For this reason, they are not so strictly limited in their distribution as are many cold-blooded species; one type of mammal or another may be found in areas with very adverse climatic conditions. Representative mammals include horses, cows, lions, elephants, deer, rabbits, whales, kangaroos and a host of similar animals.

Do Any Mammals Lay Eggs?

Only two types of mammals lay eggs: the duckbill and the spiny anteater. The duckbill, also called platypus, is found in southern Australia and Tasmania; the spiny anteater, of which there are several varieties, occurs in Australia, Tasmania and New Guinea.

Duckbills lay their eggs in nests built in burrows in the banks of streams. The female probably incubates the eggs in some fashion, but the creatures are very shy and not much is known about this part of their activities. The female spiny anteater has a small pouch on the under surface of her body, where the single egg is kept until it is hatched. The young anteater remains within the pouch for a time after hatching and gets milk from the teats in the walls of the pouch.

What Are Pouched Mammals?

The pouched mammals include the familiar kangaroos and opossums besides several other animals not well known to the average person, such as the Tasmanian devil, the bandicoot, the marsupial wolf and the phalanger. The females have a pouch on the under surface of the body called the marsupium—hence the group name, marsupial. One of the most interesting features of marsupials is that the young are born in an extremely undeveloped condi-tion; consequently, they must have a safe place where they can develop further until they are able to fend for themselves. This additional growth takes place within the pouch which contains the teats or mammary glands.

Mammals

Living marsupials are found today primarily in Australia and adjacent areas, although a few are found in South America and one—the well-known opossum—in the United States. In former times marsupials probably had an almost world-wide distribution, but they were apparently killed off over large areas by other more efficient mammals. It is thought that they have been able to survive in Australia only because they are the only large mammals native to this country. The marsupials probably migrated to Australia at a time when the continent was connected with other land areas by a land bridge, which apparently disappeared before other mammals found their way across.

How Do Opossums Mate?

The fact that the reproductive organ or penis of the male opossum is forked has resulted in some interesting suppositions regarding the reproductive habits of the animal. At the time of mating, according to one story, the forked organ of the male is inserted into the nostrils of the female, and the male cells or sperm are deposited within the nasal passages. The female then supposedly thrusts her nose into her pouch and blows vigorously. In this way, the male cells are deposited in the pouch where, it is believed, fertilization of the eggs takes place and the young pass through their complete development.

The male opossum does have a forked reproductive organ, but reproduction does not take place as outlined above. The forked penis of the male is correlated with the structure of the female reproductive tract, which branches into two parts a short distance from the outside opening, and opossums mate in the same way as do other animals.

However, what actually happens afterward is almost as amazing as the story just related.

After they are conceived, the developing young remain within the body of the female for about twelve days, and are born in a very immature stage of development.

Each of the young (from eight to as many as twenty-one) is actually smaller than a honey bee, and so unlike the adults in appearance that no one unfamiliar with this type of reproduction could possibly recognize them as opossums. At one time it was thought that the female helped the young into the pouch, but direct observation has since revealed that they clamber into it by themselves, using their strongly developed front legs to scramble through the hair. Once within the pouch, each of the young opossums swallows one of the nipples or teats, attaching themselves so firmly that it is almost impossible to pull them loose. If there are more young opossums than there are teats, which happens occasionally, only those fortunate enough to locate a mammary gland will survive; the extra infants will all die.

After remaining within the marsupium for about seventy days, the young emerge, but remain with the mother for some time. As she travels from one place to another they cling to the hair of her body. Sometimes the female curls her tail over her back and the young attach themselves to it by their own tails and dangle head downward.

Are Opossums Fooling When They Play Dead?

If an opossum is captured or attacked, it frequently does not run or fight as the majority of animals do under similar circumstances. Instead, it sinks to the ground, partially closes its eyes, allows its mouth to gape and its tongue to loll out. During this procedure, its breathing becomes almost imperceptible. It is often said that when an opossum behaves in this way it is deliberately feigning death to deceive its attackers. Some people have doubted whether opossums have this much intelligence, and believe that they really faint with fear. By tossing them into water, or unceremoniously dumping a bucket of water over them, one can usually revive the creatures. Whatever the reason for their performance, it appears decidedly disadvantageous to future generations of opossums; if deliberate, it seems to be an asinine procedure and to reflect upon the intelligence of our only marsupial. Surely any attacker, whether human or animal, would rather contend with a passive victim than with a clawing, biting or fleeing antagonist.

How Are Kangaroos Born?

Young kangaroos, like young opossums, have been found within the pouch of the mother so firmly attached to the nipples that it is almost impossible to remove them. From this has grown the belief, occasionally encountered, that the young kangaroo is not born as other mammals are, but simply grows from the belly of its mother. I need hardly say that this belief is not correct.

The birth and development of a young kangaroo are quite similar to the opossum's. At birth the infants do not even faintly resemble the adults, and the young of even the larger species are only about an inch in length. In fact, there is a greater difference in size between the newly born of a large kangaroo and the adult than is to be found in any other mammal. The grublike young have enlarged claws on the front feet which enable them, like the baby opossums, to scramble through the hair and find their own way into the pouch.

The length of time they spend in the pouch varies with the kind of kangaroo and, for the larger species, may be as much as several months. As the young kangaroo gains in size, it spends less and less time in the pouch, although even when it is quite large it sometimes bounces into the pouch when danger threatens, or occasionally sticks its head in for a drink of milk.

Can Kangaroos Be Taught to Box?

Some readers have probably seen a boxing kangaroo on exhibition, and may have listened with sympathy to the harangue of the owner who dramatically told of numberless hours of grueling labor spent in training his prodigy. Possibly he even claimed that his particular kangaroo was the only boxing kangaroo in the world. Such claims are far from true. Even wild kangaroos are quite adept at boxing, and sometimes amuse themselves by sparring with each other. While a kangaroo may become more manageable with training, it is very questionable whether its boxing ability is improved by the attentions of the trainer.

Can Kangaroos Climb Trees?

Some kangaroos are able to climb trees and, though they are quite awkward about it, even seem to prefer the trees to the ground. The tree kangaroos, or tree wallabies as they are sometimes called, have long claws and their front legs are comparatively longer than those of other kangaroos. Some species are rather large, having a body length of approximately four feet and a tail of about the same length.

Is There a Manlike Ape?

If we are to believe some fiction writers, there is a kind of manlike ape in Africa of the same general type as the chimpanzee, except that it is larger and considerably more intelligent. It is not a gorilla, for the gorilla sometimes appears in the stories as the villain. These fabulous apes are supposed to feed chiefly upon meat, and when a large animal is killed they hold a tribal dance. The females squat about in a circle and beat upon improvised drums, while the males dance themselves into a frenzy before they dismember and devour their prey. The males or bulls also amuse themselves by fighting, beating their chests with their fists and roaring challenges to the moon.

Of course, no such humanoid ape exists. There are only three types of apes to which the term manlike can be sensibly applied—the gorilla, the chimpanzee, and the orangutan. The gibbon is classified with these others, but it is smaller and not so well known to the average person. All these apes are primarily vegetarians rather than meat eaters, although most of them are not averse to eggs, grubs or even small mammals and birds. None of them kill large animals for food, so far as is known, and although they are sometimes found in family groups, there is no evidence that any of them ever hold tribal or ceremonial dances.

How Big Is the Biggest Ape?

The gorilla is by far the largest of the great apes, but there is no evidence that it ever reaches a height of nine feet, as some sensationally minded writers have maintained. Captive gorillas, thanks to the inactive life that they are forced to live, are usually heavier than wild specimens.

In 1941 there were eleven large gorillas in captivity in the United States. It will probably be a surprise to many people to learn that Gargantua, certainly the most ballyhooed gorilla in the world, was not the largest gorilla in captivity at that time; he was, as a matter of fact, a rather poor third as far as weight is concerned. In 1941, Mbongo and Nagagi, two gorillas in the San Diego Zoo, weighed 618 and 585 pounds as compared with Gargantua's 500 pounds. Since then, Mbongo and Nagagi have both died, so that by the time this book goes to press Gargantua may be the largest living gorilla in this country.

The greatest accurate weight for a wild gorilla that I have noted is 460 pounds; the greatest height is six feet three and three-fourths inches for a specimen that was estimated to weigh 450 pounds. The six-foot-three-and-three-fourth-inch gorilla had a chest measurement of sixty-one inches and an arm span of ninety inches from tip to tip of its outstretched fingers. While the average man cannot be compared with the gorilla in most measurements, human beings have comparatively longer legs, and a greater cranial capacity.

Are Gorillas Dangerous?

There has been considerable discussion regarding the temperament and ferocity of gorillas, and for many years it was thought that they held a continuous open season on man. When the existence of these enormous apes first became established, it was firmly believed that they habitually watched jungle trails from overhanging trees so that they could seize and kill unwary human beings who passed beneath.

Several men have recently studied the habits of gorillas, and it is now known that many of the early ideas about them were far from true. Although gorillas do sometimes climb trees in search of fruit, and occasionally build nests in low bushes or trees for the females and young, they apparently do not travel through trees to any extent. Indeed, their great weight makes tree life impossible.

In the majority of cases, gorillas will melt quietly into the forest rather than attack a human being without provocation. But they will certainly bluff, and they may do everything short of attack in trying to frighten a human being away. They have been known to stir up a frightful noise by stamping their feet and thrashing around in the bushes, and to top off these preliminaries by charging with bloodcurdling roars, only to stop short suddenly, just before attacking, and make off quietly into the forest.

There have been one or two instances, however, which show that an occasional gorilla may not need much excuse to attack a human being. The late Harry Raven, who killed one of the largest wild gorillas ever weighed, had a hair-raising experience collecting the animal. He was crawling under a fallen tree when a terrific roar sounded almost in his ear. Scrambling to his feet, he saw an enormous gorilla looming above him and coming fast. Raven fired quickly, and the gorilla fell, then staggered to its feet. He fired again and the great ape went down, this time for good, but only fifteen feet away. I do not believe that this gorilla was bluffing.

What Is the Most Dangerous Animal in the Sea?

Killer whales fully deserve their name, and are aptly described as the wolves of the sea. Many people who have studied them consider them the most ferocious animals in the ocean. They prey upon seals, porpoises, fish and similar creatures, and their appetites are enormous, although their maximum size is about thirty feet, which is not large, as whales go. The stomach of one, variously reported to be from sixteen to twenty-one feet long, was found to contain thirteen seals and fourteen porpoises!

One might think that the size of the larger whales would make them immune to attack from any animal, but a pack of killer whales does not hesitate to challenge any whale that crosses its path. Peculiarly enough, they seem to prefer the tongues of these enormous whales. Eyewitnesses to combats between them have seen killer whales slash continuously at the mouths of the larger whales, tearing off pieces of flesh until the tongue of the victim was exposed. A few more rushes and the tongue was torn out, leaving the hapless whale a floating dying hulk. Roy Chapman Andrews saw killer whales attacking a group of California gray whales, a species that attains a length of fifty feet. He later had a chance to examine thirty-five of these gray whales and found that, of this number, seven had contributed their tongues to the insatiable appetites of the killers.

Killer whales will attack anything in the water, including human beings, and although I have not noted any instances of their having killed a man it very probably has happened. Herbert F. Pointing, on an antarctic expedition, had an unenviable experience with a herd of eight of these monsters. He was standing on an ice floe photographing them when the whole group dived under him. The block of ice heaved suddenly, broke into several parts, and the heads of the killer whales appeared between the broken pieces. The whales then attacked, trying to dislodge him as he made his way frantically from piece to piece of floating ice. Just as he jumped to solid ground, the head of one of the whales rose out of the water and hung with wide-open jaws over the spot he had just left. The other seven, one after the other, broke the surface, but after seeing that the man was rapidly putting a safe distance between himself and the water they quit the spot for more fertile fields.

Killer whales belong to the so-called toothed whales, a group that includes the sperm whale or cachalot, the narwhale and several types of dolphins and porpoises. They are rather easily distinguished from most of their relatives by a large triangular top fin, and their bodies are conspicuously colored with black and white markings.

The toothless whales have no true teeth, but they have instead a number of sheets of whalebone or baleen attached to the upper jaw. The sulphur bottom or blue whale, the right whale, the California gray whale, the humpbacked whale and the finback are all toothless or whalebone whales.

The World's Largest Animals Feed on the Smallest

Whalebone or baleen whales are the largest animals alive, but they feed upon very small organisms such as shrimp, small fish and similar creatures. It is obvious that an animal the size of a whale would have trouble filling its enormous stomach with such tiny food particles unless it had a special way to concentrate the material. However, the sheets of whalebone or baleen attached to its upper jaw help it in gathering these small food animals. The sheets are set very close together, and each of them has many long bristles attached to one edge. To secure its food, the whale opens its mouth and swims through schools of small organisms. When it has a mouth full of water, it closes its mouth, raises its enormous tongue, and lets the water rush out between the plates, the particles of food being retained in the mouth by the straining action of the baleen.

Whalebone, so called, is not true bone at all, but a flexible horny material similar to the fingernails of man. It was formerly in great demand for use as stays in women's corsets, but the few women who now insist upon wearing them find that the more romantic whalebone stays have been replaced by thin steel reinforcements. Baleen is now sometimes used for making cigarette cases and other trinkets.

What Is Ambergris?

Ambergris is a whale product, a waxy substance now used chiefly in the manufacture of perfumery. Its only known source is the digestive tract of the sperm whale or cachalot, but the details of its formation are not entirely understood. The presence of ambergris is generally considered evidence of illness on the part of the whale, and it probably is formed as a direct result of the animal's food habits. The sperm whale feeds principally upon large squids, whose mouths are surrounded by big horny beaks. Because undigested beaks are frequently found in a lump of ambergris, the theory is that they set up an irritation in the intestine or some other organ which stimulates the secretion of ambergris as a protective covering.

Aside from being found in the body of the whale itself, a lump of ambergris is sometimes discovered floating in the sea or washed up on a beach, presumably thrown off by a whale. Many seafaring men have felt their hearts jump into their mouths at the sight of a large, irregular-shaped grayish mass floating on the water, for the material is worth from fifteen to thirty-five dollars an ounce, depending on the amount available. The hearts of the majority, however, have shortly dropped into their boots when the substance was identified as a mass of soap, fat or other valueless material. Nevertheless, anything found in the ocean or on the shore that resembles fat or soap should be taken for identification to a museum, despite the possible apoplectic comments of the overworked staff.

Most pieces of ambergris that have been found have been rather small, but a few large masses have been discovered. The largest of which there is definite record weighed approximately 900 pounds, and was found near the coast of New Zealand. The largest piece known to have been taken from the body of a whale weighed about 750 pounds. This lump was found by the crew of a whaling ship and was probably of sufficient value to make the men forget all about whaling for the remainder of the voyage. Only recently a 252-pound piece was found by two Long Island fishermen.

What Is the Biggest Baby in the World?

A young whale at birth is often almost half as long as its mother. A female sperm whale only thirty-two feet in length was found to contain a calf that was fourteen feet eight inches long. Another baby, taken from an eighty-foot blue whale, was twenty-five feet in length and weighed sixteen thousand pounds. This tremendous size is possible only because the water in which the whales live helps to support the weight of the developing embryo. No land mammal could possibly carry such a large embryo. Indeed, the size which adult whales attain is possible only because they live in a supporting medium.

The whale's growth to maturity is unbelievably rapid. It may double its length within a year and, in some species, the female may become mature at the end of the second or third year of life. This rapid growth is probably one reason that whales have not become extinct as a result of the enormous numbers killed by man. It is thought that the pregnancy period is from ten to sixteen months, but more observations on this point are needed.

How Are Young Whales Fed?

Young whales are fed on milk, like the young of other animals. Because the teats of the females are on the under surface of the body near the rear end, for a long time it was a mystery how the young whale, which breathes air, could procure a meal without drowning. It is now known that at feeding time the huge mother rolls over on her side to bring the nipples close to the surface of the water. The young whale then grasps one of the nipples in its mouth, its nostrils remaining above the water. Special muscles pump the milk down its throat, which relieves it of the pulling effort that the human infant must exert.

How Does a Whale "Blow"?

The expression "thar she blows," shouted by a lookout in the crow's-nest of a whaling ship, is probably familiar to most people, who also generally take it to mean that the whale is spouting water from its nostrils. That is not what happens. Whales never deliberately take water into the breathing passages; if they did, they would drown just as surely as would a human being. When a whale starts to dive or sound, it fills its lungs with air, which it retains while it is under water; then when it comes to the surface it expels the air with some force, or "blows." The air that is expelled, warmed and moistened from being in the whale's lungs, condenses upon contact with the colder outside air and forms streams of vapor resembling water which can be seen for some distance. The same thing happens on a small scale when our own breaths condense on a cool frosty morning. If the whale happens to blow a short distance below the water surface, a considerable amount of water may be carried upward with the escaping air; and people seeing this have thought that the water came from the whale's nostrils.

How Deep Can Whales Dive?

Protected as they are from the terrific pressure of the water by a layer of fat or blubber sometimes twenty inches thick just beneath the skin, whales can dive to tremendous depths. This was suspected long before it was proved, since the large squids upon which the sperm whale feeds are usually found in very deep water. Positive proof of the whale's deep-diving ability, however, was obtained when in 1932 a blundering sperm whale became entangled in a submarine cable on the ocean floor, 3200 feet down. The cable was broken and, when it was hauled to the surface for repairs, the drowned whale was still caught in it. Some authorities believe that whales can dive even deeper than this.

Such an accomplishment by a mere flesh-and-blood mammal can be appreciated when we remember that the sperm whale reached a depth more than two hundred feet deeper than that reached by the famous metal bathysphere, which was especially constructed for deep-sea diving.

Can a Whale Swallow a Man?

The question of whether or not a whale can swallow a man has been discussed since the time of Jonah. As far as Jonah is concerned, there is also the problem of whether a whale or fish was involved. It is not possible for the whalebone or toothless whales to swallow a man, because their throats are less than a foot in diameter. Any human being larger than a small child or a midget would cause them considerable embarrassment if they were to become ambitious enough to try. Small penguins are the largest animals that have ever been found in the stomach of a toothless whale.

The great sperm whale or cachalot, however, is an entirely different matter, for the throat of this whale is large enough to swallow a man whole. Captured sperm whales have been found to contain pieces of squid larger than the body of a human being.

Some people doubt that there are any verified accounts of a whale's swallowing a man, but two reports are of interest. In 1891 the boat of a whaling ship was upset by the flip of the tail of a large sperm whale, and when the crew was rescued one of the men was missing. Despite this loss, however, the rest of the men rallied and several hours later captured the whale that had wrecked their boat. They fell to work upon the carcass, and by the next morning they had reached the innards of the creature. Deciding to remove the whale's stomach, they hauled it on deck. Something inside started to move, much to everyone's astonishment, and when they opened it up there was their lost comrade, unconscious, but still with sufficient vitality to have made the movement that saved him. The man eventually recovered, so the story goes, but parts of his skin remained a dead white color for the rest of his life, supposedly as a result of the action of the whale's gastric juices upon the body surfaces not protected by clothing.

The most unbelievable part of the whole story is that the man should have been alive after he had been in the whale's stomach for so many hours. Perhaps the whale obligingly swallowed enough air for the man's needs, and his nostrils conveniently remained above the digestive juices while the rest of his face was being digested!

An account of a whale swallowing a man recently appeared in Natural History Magazine, related by a man who was allegedly a former ship's surgeon. According to the story, a sperm whale swallowed one of the crewmen. The whale was later captured and the badly mangled body of the man was recovered. However, later investigation by Dr. Edward M. Weyer, Editor of Natural History Magazine, indicated that the story teller used a fictitious name. Chances are good that this instance never did occur.

What Is the Largest Animal That Ever Lived?

The sulphur bottom or blue whale is the largest animal alive today and, so far as is known, the largest animal that ever lived. The longest whale of which I have found authentic record measured 108 feet and weighed approximately eighty tons or 160,000 pounds. Another, more corpulent specimen of ninety-five feet tipped the scales at approximately 294,000 pounds. Sperm whales, the largest of the toothed whales, do not grow so large as their toothless cousins. The largest sperm whale of which I have a record was a male that was washed ashore near Port Arthur, Texas, in 1910. It was sixty-three and one-half feet long—without question a fine specimen—but Dr. H. H. Newman, the good professor who measured it, became too enthusiastic when he stated that the sperm whale was probably the largest creature that ever lived.

Some extinct reptiles belonging to the dinosaur group— the thunder beasts or thunder lizards—were very large, but there is no evidence that any of them were as large as the blue whale. Several rather complete skeletons of these reptiles have been found, from which it has been possible to estimate the maximum size they attained. One of the largest known skeletons measures eighty-seven and one-half feet. It has also been estimated that the heaviest of the dinosaurs may have reached a weight of fifty tons, which is considerably less than the known weights of several kinds of whales.

Did the Unicorn Ever Exist?

The unicorn, according to mythology, was a horselike creature with a single horn growing from its forehead. No such creature has ever existed; but the term unicorn or unicorn fish is sometimes applied to the narwhale, a type of toothed whale, which grows to a length of fifteen or sixteen feet and is found primarily in arctic waters. The peculiar development of one of its teeth is responsible for the name of unicorn. At birth, both male and female narwhales have a few teeth, but they very shortly degenerate, except for two in the upper jaw. These two seldom become functional in the female, but in the male the left tooth continues to grow. It grows forward straight through the upper jaw and lip, spiraling upon itself in a clockwise direction. The right tooth normally does not develop even in the male, but occasional specimens have been collected in which both teeth had grown into tusks, and for some unknown reason both the tusks spiraled in the same direction. Exact measurements are scant, but it is probable that the tusks sometimes grow to a length of nine or ten feet.

The function of this enormous tooth is not definitely known. There have been reports that it is used as a weapon for fighting, for punching holes in the ice, and for spearing fish, but, so far as I am aware, none of these reports have been confirmed.

The narwhale has figured rather conspicuously in connection with the mythical unicorn of European folklore. Norsemen from Iceland, where the narwhales were at one time rather numerous, collected some of the teeth and took them to Europe, trading them as genuine unicorn horns to the delighted Europeans. The chances are that no true description was given of the original owner of the "horn," since, according to mythology, the unicorn was supposed to be a graceful, horselike creature, not at all like the legless, clumsy, blunt-faced narwhale.

How Did the Mermaid Legend Originate?

The story of mermaids is one of the oldest legends to be told by seafaring men. According to romantic descriptions these fabulous creatures have the faces and bodies of beautiful women, while the legs and feet have been replaced by fishlike tails. Strangely, descriptions of male mermaids or mermen seldom appear, possibly because the originators of the stories were more interested in the fair sex during a long ocean voyage.

Such creatures do not exist, but animals live in the ocean that could very well have been the basis for the story. There are a few species of aquatic mammals, called sea cows, that are found along the coasts of various areas of the world. These include the dugong, widely distributed in parts of the Indian Ocean and near the shores of Australia, and two kinds of manatee occurring in the rivers and along the coast of South America, and sometimes are found in Florida. Although even a drunken sailor could not mistake the face of a sea cow for that of a beautiful maiden at close range, it is believed that these animals are responsible for the mermaid story. When the creatures come to the surface to breathe, they stick their rounded heads above the surface, and they may remain in this upright position for some time. At a distance the head might easily be mistaken for that of a human being, and this resemblance is heightened when a female appears at the surface holding a youngster in her front flipper. A nearer view of such a female would certainly cause the observer to hope that this ugly old sea hag was only the nurse maid carrying the youngster out for a stroll, although it is a mystery how anyone could think that any relative of the youngster could possibly be beautiful.

Do Elephants Drink Through Their Trunks?

Elephants do not drink through their trunks, as people sometimes suppose, but they do suck water up into their trunks and then squirt it into their mouths. They also use their trunks as a spray. If undisturbed, they may spend hours in a lake or river enjoying the cooling and cleansing effect of the water. Captive elephants who were being teased by human beings have been known to fill their trunks with water and squirt it fire-hose fashion full in the faces of their tormentors. Contrary to popular opinion, however, a young elephant uses its mouth—not its trunk— to suck milk from its mother's teats.

With its trunk an elephant can pull down a big tree or delicately pick a small peanut from the floor and pop it into its mouth. In the wilds, it uses its trunk to strip from trees and bushes, and thrust into its mouth, the leaves, twigs and other vegetation upon which it feeds.

Elephants do not grow nearly so slowly as they are commonly supposed to, but may reach maturity when twelve to fifteen years of age. The period of pregnancy or gestation of elephants varies considerably and is one of the longest for mammals. However, it is not as long as has been reported. Direct observations of captive elephants show that the average gestation period is from twenty to twenty-four months.

At birth young elephants weigh from 150 to 200 pounds. The trunk is not so long proportionally as is the adult's, and observers say that it is an almost useless appendage, continually getting in the way until the elephant has learned how to use it. I doubt whether even a biologist would have the patience to count the number of muscles in an elephant's trunk, but one writer says that there are more than forty thousand. In view of the varied and manifold ways in which an elephant employs its trunk, this seems a reasonable estimate.

Circuses Use Indian Elephants

The elephants seen in circuses are almost invariably Indian rather than African elephants. African elephants are not domesticated to the extent that Indian elephants are; consequently, the former species are much more difficult to obtain.

It is not difficult to distinguish between these two kinds of elephants, although the distinctions are not important for most people. In profile, the back of the Indian elephant is strongly arched, and there is a definite depression between the head and the shoulders. In the African species, there is no depression, and the back is not arched. The highest point of the back of an African elephant is just above the shoulders instead of near the center of the back.

Also, African elephants have larger ears than the Indian species; in large males they may be three feet wide. Finally, there are four toenails on each of the hind feet of the Indian elephant, while its African cousin has but three.

How Do Elephants Use Their Tusks?

Elephants' tusks are modified teeth, the longest and heaviest teeth in the entire animal kingdom. They are used in fighting and in digging up roots, bulbs and similar plant products which elephants eat. It has also been reported that the African species occasionally picks up the young elephants with its tusks and carries them for some distance.

Practically all male African elephants have tusks, and even the female often develops them. The female Indian elephant, however, seldom does, and even the male of this species is frequently without them.

The longest known tusks from present-day elephants are a pair from an African elephant now in the National Collection of Heads and Horns, Bronx Park, New York. The longest of the pair measures eleven feet five and one-half inches; its mate, eleven feet. Their combined weight is 293 pounds, which is rather light for such long tusks. The heaviest tusk known, which is in the British Museum, weighs 226½ pounds, and the second of the pair weighs 214, for a combined record weight of 440½ pounds.

The tusks of some of the extinct mammoths were much longer than those of living elephants. The longest known tusk is one from an imperial mammoth and is a fraction of an inch over sixteen feet. Discovered in Texas several years ago, this enormous tooth is now on display in the American Museum of Natural History.

Besides being longer, the tusks of the mammoths were considerably more curved than those of present-day elephants. In some species, the tusks grew outward and downward from the base, then curved inward toward each other. Frequently, the ends of the tusks crossed in front of the head. In long tusks, the curvature was sometimes so great that the points were directed back toward the bases of the tusks. It is difficult to understand how they could have been of use to their owners at this stage.

Are Elephants Afraid of Mice?

It is popularly believed that an elephant is much afraid of mice, presumably because it fears the mouse might get into the end of its trunk and either suffocate it or injure the delicate inner lining of the nasal passages. But the actions of elephants in zoological gardens and circuses do not confirm this belief. Mice are frequently seen running about in elephants' stalls, sometimes very close to the ends of their trunks, but the elephants totally disregard them. Since their eyesight is rather poor, it is possible that they cannot see a mouse at a distance; but since their sense of smell is one of the keenest in the entire animal kingdom the chances are that they can smell it, small as it is, especially when it is only a few inches from the end of the trunk. But in any case, it is very doubtful whether a mouse could cause an elephant much injury, even if the rodent had the courage to crawl into the end of the trunk. In all probability the elephant would simply take a deep breath, blow vigorously through the trunk and splatter the mouse over the walls of the stall.

Mammals

Do Elephants Ever Forget?

Elephants do have a good memory, and some of them may remember an injury for a long time. The late Dr. Raymond Ditmars used to tell of an elephant in the New York Zoological Park which, for some unknown reason, took an intense dislike to one of the attendants. The attendant left the park, but returned some years later. When he visited the elephant house, he was almost instantly recognized by the enraged elephant, which tried to break out of the enclosure to get at him. But the elephant's memory has been considerably exaggerated. The process of training wild elephants may be quite severe, and if they never forgot injuries and abuse very few of them would ever be tamed. Some elephants doubtless have better memories than others, but that an elephant never forgets is a statement without foundation.

Have Elephants a Common Graveyard?

According to legend, all old and dying elephants have a special place where they go to die. However, no such graveyard has ever been found except in movies and highly imaginative stories, and the chances are that the acres and acres of tusks supposedly reposing therein exist only in dreams. Why, then, are dead elephants never found? The answer is that they are sometimes found, despite popular belief to the contrary. The bodies of those elephants that are never found are probably quickly eaten by the other animals of the jungle, and their skeletons and tusks rapidly covered by forest litter and growing vegetation.

Do White Elephants Exist?

No elephant that was really white has ever been seen, but the name is applied to elephants that are lighter in color than is normal. The real color of a so-called white elephant is light gray or yellowish, sometimes with pink spots.

In former times, white elephants were held in high esteem; they were regarded as sacred and even worshiped. So valuable were they considered that, in some regions, only the kings were considered worthy to own one. Actually, kings were probably the only persons wealthy enough to keep white elephants in the luxury that custom demanded. White elephants were never worked, and were given special quarters, sometimes as elaborately decorated as palaces. Special servants were assigned to administer to their needs, and their food was frequently served in troughs of silver or on spotless white cloths.

One can easily see why the expression "white elephant" has come to mean an object that is expensive to keep yet yields no returns; or one that is difficult to dispose of. P. T. Barnum "had a white elephant on his hands" when he attempted to obtain one for his circus. The first elephant died en route to the United States, and by the time one at last arrived in the country it had, according to reports, cost him two hundred thousand dollars—a fabulous sum even for a white elephant.

How Dangerous Is a Rhinoceros?

There has been considerable debate among big game hunters over the pugnacity of rhinoceroses. Some believe they are the most dangerous of all animals, while others insist that hunting rhinoceroses is no more dangerous than hunting ducks. Most hunters think that, of the African mammals, the elephant, lion, buffalo, hippopotamus and rhinoceros are the most dangerous; and the rhinoceros has been ranked both at the head and at the foot of this list. Obviously, hunters who have had a harrowing experience with a particularly ill-tempered specimen consider the rhinoceros more dangerous than do sportsmen who have been more fortunate. Some men believe that frequently what is reported as a rhinoceros charge is simply an attempt by the rhinoceros to escape; that because of poor eyesight, or sheer stupidity, the animal sometimes runs toward the hunter accidently. However, any man or animal in the path of such a charge, accidental or not, would certainly be spitted by a horn or trampled in the dust.

One hunter tells of a narrow escape he had with a white African rhinoceros. He was hunting on horseback, when he sighted a fine male. Putting spurs to his horse, he came within shooting distance, took aim and fired and expected the rhinoceros either to fall dead or retreat as members of the species usually do. But this rhinoceros had other ideas. It lowered its head and charged the horse and rider so quickly that they could not escape its rush. The longest horn caught the horse in the side, completely penetrated its body, and struck the man's leg on the opposite side. Horse and rider went down in a scrambled heap, but fortunately the hunter managed to disentangle himself in time to kill the rhinoceros before it could finish what it had started.

Rhinoceroses seem to be suspicious of anything new. When roads were first built through rhinoceros country, there were many reports of their blindly charging automobiles and reducing the cars to wreckage, and there is at least one record of an irate rhino's actually attacking a train. The passengers were made rudely aware of the attack by a tremendous jolt and, looking out of the windows, saw a rhinoceros scramble to its feet and stagger off with much snorting and head shaking.

As the story of the hunter would suggest, the horns of a rhinoceros are lethal weapons. To a white rhinoceros, and a female at that, must be awarded the prize for having produced the longest one known. This enormous horn, collected in South Africa, is sixty-two and one-fourth inches in length and it has a maximum girth of twenty-two and one-fourth inches. It is considerably longer than its nearest competitor, also from a white rhinoceros, which has a length of fifty-six and one-half inches. The horns of other species are shorter than those of the white rhinoceros, but one black rhinoceros horn of fifty-three and one-half inches is on record.

How Dangerous Is a Hippopotamus?

Hippopotamuses are generally mild or even timid, but they are also unpredictable. There are several known instances of their having made unprovoked attacks upon people, usually people in boats. In regions where the animals have not learned to fear man, there is always a certain danger from solitary individuals or from a herd aroused suddenly from their sleep.

Sir Samuel Baker, an early African explorer, writes that an irate hippopotamus once charged a steamer that he was on, knocking several parts from one of the paddle wheels, and breaking a number of holes in the bottom of the vessel with its tusks. On another occasion, some natives under his direction were driving cattle across a stream when a herd of hippopotamuses deliberately attacked the cows. They seized several of them and carried them under the water before they were finally driven off.

Does the Hippopotamus Sweat Blood?

Since biblical times there have been those who maintained that the hippopotamus could sweat blood. Various circuses with hippopotamuses on exhibit have encouraged this belief and it has not been especially discouraged by the authors of certain natural history books, who have emphasized half truths for the sake of sensationalism. During warm weather, the hippo's skin does secrete a reddish, oily liquid which probably makes the skin more resistant to water and also possibly protects it from the air. But this secretion is not blood, although it resembles blood in general appearance.

Are There Any Wild Camels in the United States?

There are two kinds of true camels, the Arabian camel with a single hump, and the two-humped camel or bactrian. The term dromedary is often applied to the bactrian camel, but a dromedary is really a breed of one-humped camel that has been developed especially for riding and racing. Bactrian camels are never correctly called dromedaries. Neither the dromedary nor the bactrian has a hump at birth; the hump develops gradually as the camel gets older.

It is thought probable that neither species of camel now exists in the original wild state, although in some areas there are wild camels which are probably offspring of domesticated camels that escaped from captivity. Large numbers of these undomesticated camels existed at one time, and probably still occur in numbers in Turkestan, the Gobi Desert and adjacent areas.

At one time there were a number of undomesticated camels in southwestern and western United States. These animals were descended from a herd that was imported by the United States Government in 1856 and used as pack animals in expeditions across arid regions of the country. This experiment was eventually abandoned, but for many years an occasional camel appeared in the area to startle inhabitants and travelers. Some of these reports are relatively recent, but it is not recommended that a camel-hunting expedition be organized on the assumption that herds of camels are still roaming the deserts of the west and southwest.

Although no true camels are native to the western hemisphere, they have relatives in South America—the alpaca, the llama, the vicuña and the guanaco. None of these animals has humps, but only a glance at their facial expression and their feet is required to see the similarity between them and the camels. Of these four "American camels," the llama and the alpaca are domesticated while the vicuña and the guanaco are found in the wild state.

How Long Can Camels Go Without Water?

It is true that camels can go without water for some time, but this capacity has been considerably exaggerated.

Mammals

Most authorities agree that, under usual desert working conditions, the maximum time between drinks for the average camel is eight or ten days. If it were not required to work during this period, it could probably last longer. According to one writer, one group of camels considerably exceeded the usual period. This particular caravan was on the march for thirty-four days without water, and during this time covered 530 miles; however, the majority of the camels died before the end of the journey.

For many years people have been trying to explain how the camel can survive as long as he does without water. One suggestion is that excess water is stored in the hump, the idea being that the hump is simply a built-in reservoir into which the water pours as it is drunk. Another suggestion has been that extra water is stored in the small pouches that open into the camel's stomach. Neither of these suggestions is entirely correct, although the stomach, the hump and various other tissues all play some part. Excess food and water that the camel does not need at once are stored within the body as fat and other substances, to be drawn on in time of need. Much of this material passes to the hump, which becomes large and plump when the camel gets enough to eat and drink. But there is no hollow water cooler or reservoir concealed within it. When the body draws upon its food reserve, a considerable amount of water is produced, and this is what the camel utilizes when it cannot get water from other sources. Some water is also stored in other body tissues and in the stomach pouches—all of which enables the camel to survive during the dry periods.

Animal Facts *and* Fallacies

What Animals Never Drink Water?

Camels are not the only animals that can go without water for a relatively long time. A few others have this capacity so well developed that camels are rank amateurs in comparison. Many wild animals including giraffes, mountain sheep and goats, and wild cattle have been known to go without drinking for several days, and some desert species such as gazelles, ground squirrels, mice and rats do not drink at all so far as is known.

A small gazelle which was kept for six months by the Central Asiatic Expedition in the Gobi Desert always refused water when it was offered. A colony of pocket mice from New Mexico, which were kept for a time in the American Museum, consistently refused water, even though they were fed on seeds that had been thoroughly dried. These animals are apparently able to get enough water for their needs in the digestion and utilization of their food. But it is quite possible that even they would have to drink occasionally if they were forced to do the work of a camel.

Llamas Defend Themselves by Spitting

One of the most interesting, but not one of the nicest, habits of the llama, a relative of the camel, is its ability to spit with an accuracy that might well be the envy of human tobacco-chewing marksmen. Visitors who annoy llamas in zoological gardens are quite likely to receive a copious shower of saliva, which the llama can spit through its teeth for some distance. It has even been reported that at times a llama will chastise a persistent rider by turning

[34]

its head and spitting full in the face of its astonished persecutor. Since the saliva is quite irritating, such a bath is decidedly unpleasant.

Deer Grow New Horns Each Year

It is difficult to believe that the antlers of the deer are shed and regrown each year, but there have been so many observations of the process in captive deer that we now know it is a normal occurrence. It might not seem so remarkable if the antlers were only a few inches long, but the antlers of the mature elk may be over five feet long and the antlers of the moose may have a spread of more than six feet. Even more astounding is the probability that the now extinct Irish elk, whose antlers had a spread of over nine feet, also shed and replaced them each year.

Just before the antlers are shed, a portion of the main antler shaft near the head becomes weakened by the destruction and absorption of the bony material. The antlers eventually break at this weakened point without any loss of blood, and apparently without pain to the animal. The stumps that remain become covered with skin, and it is from these covered stumps that the new antlers begin to grow. The growth of the new antlers is unbelievably rapid. Observations have shown that they may grow as much as one-third to one-half an inch a day. Until development of the antlers is complete, they are covered by a layer of skin, called the velvet, which drops off in strips once full growth is attained, leaving a solid, bony, sharp-tipped antler.

How Do Mountain Sheep Show Their Age?

The approximate age of some mountain sheep can be determined by an examination of the horns, but the ease with which this can be done varies. I have seen sheep heads with horns so well marked that an inexperienced person could easily estimate the age, but I have also seen others that would trouble even an expert. The horn growth for each year is marked by a deep crack or crevice that encircles the horn, the material between two cracks being called a ridge. When the cracks and ridges are definite, the age of the sheep can be approximately determined by counting the ridges, one ridge for each year of life. But in addition to the large cracks and ridges that mark the yearly growth there are usually numerous smaller rings and ridges on the horn surface. These sometimes are, but should not be, confused with the annual rings; the annual rings are wider and deeper and the annual ridges may be an inch or an inch and a half in width.

Do Wild Sheep Land on Their Horns When They Jump?

Wild sheep never deliberately land on their horns when they jump. The sheep that does, does so by accident, and it will certainly end up with a broken neck. This belief, occasionally encountered, probably originated from the fact that, when frightened, mountain sheep do sometimes dive head first from a cliff, but to survive for other leaps the animals must land on their feet.

The head of a fine mountain sheep is one of the most prized trophies in the sporting world. A wild sheep found in the mountains of southern Russia and northern India, called Marco Polo's argali, grows the longest horns of any of the mountain sheep. The largest one known is seventy-five inches long, following the curves of the horn, and it has a maximum girth of sixteen inches, an enormous size for animals weighing only 300 to 350 pounds.

Do Bears Hibernate?

Bears are said to hibernate during the winter, particularly during the extremely cold weather in the northern parts of their range. Strictly speaking, however, the winter sleep of bears is not true hibernation. Their temperatures and breathing remain relatively normal, and during warm spells some bears may emerge and remain outside for a day or so before returning to their sleeping quarters. Bears are much more easily disturbed during their winter sleep than is commonly thought, and may scare the wits out of a trustful human being who approaches too closely. If the investigator is persistent, he may be severely injured by the outraged bear whose sleep he has disturbed.

The cubs are born during this winter sleep. If one considers the size of the parents, they are very poor excuses for offspring, being smaller than the young of a porcupine and sometimes weighing no more than six or eight *ounces* at birth.

Although polar bears are exposed to far worse weather conditions than others bears, only pregnant females sleep during the winter. They dig a hole in the ice and snow and remain there for several months, during which time the young are born and develop sufficiently to be taken outside.

The Bear Hug

It is commonly thought that bears, especially the grizzlies, need no excuse to attack a human being. There have, it is true, been a few instances of grizzly and polar bears' attacking people without provocation, but such cases are rare. All species of bears normally avoid man and, unless they are wounded or cornered, will retreat if given a chance. An angry or wounded bear, however, is one of the most dangerous antagonists on earth, and it may attack without hesitation.

According to popular story, the bear first seizes its victim and squeezes him to death with the famous "bear hug," and then devours him. However, there is no evidence to back up the story at all. A bear kills with its front paws—with which it can strike one of the most lethal blows in the animal kingdom—sometimes aided by claws and teeth. Inasmuch as a bear has been known to break the neck of a huge bison bull with a single blow, it is apparent that it would be ridiculous for it to try to kill any animal or human being by squeezing it to death.

Grizzly bears seldom eat human beings whom they have killed, although they will eat anything else, from insects to putrid flesh.

Can Adult Bears Climb Trees?

Bears have a reputation as tree climbers, and I well remember listening as a child to an elderly friend describe how he climbed a tree with a bear after him. In this particular escapade, according to my friend, the bear pursued him to the topmost branches and, balked by the

[38]

smaller limbs, was trying to shake him from the tree when friends arrived conveniently and shot it.

The black bear is an excellent tree climber, even as an adult, and will sometimes sleep astride a limb barely large enough to support its weight, but grizzlies seldom climb trees even when they are young. Thus the only bears in North America that would normally be able to climb a tree after a man are the black bears. These creatures are usually inoffensive, however, and I have never heard of an authentic instance of their doing so. I am more than suspicious that my friend's story was exaggerated, if indeed it had any factual foundation.

How Much Do Grizzly Bears Weigh?

One cannot read much about grizzly bears before coming upon a statement that someone has killed one weighing from 1700 to 1800 pounds. Most of these alleged weights are based upon hunters' estimates, and the following instance illustrates why the estimates should be regarded with suspicion. Several years ago a very large grizzly bear in a zoological park was weighed and found to tip the scales at 1153 pounds. Several hunters who saw it admitted that it was larger than some which they had estimated to weigh 1800 pounds. This captive specimen is probably the largest grizzly bear that has ever been weighed by an unbiased person, and it was doubtless considerably fatter than it would have been in the wild state.

The great brown bears of Alaska, relatives of the grizzlies, are larger than the true grizzlies, but even they fall short of the fabulous 1800 pounds mark. The largest specimen of which I am aware weighed 1656 pounds; and it is said that they sometimes attain a length of ten feet six inches. The polar bears are close competitors of the brown bears in size, and some people believe that they may even be larger. They too have been measured at ten feet six inches, and weights of 1600 pounds have been recorded.

What Mammals Can Fly?

Bats are the only mammals that fly in the true sense of the word, although there are other mammals that can glide through the air to some extent. Gliding mammals include the so-called flying squirrels and the flying lemurs, the latter peculiar creatures about the size of a cat, found in the Malay Peninsula and adjacent areas.

The wings of a bat are different in structure from the wings of a bird. Bat wings consist of leathery, membranous skin supported by the bones of the front limbs and by other enormously long bones that correspond to the finger bones of man. All the finger bones except those of the thumb serve as braces for the wings; the thumbs, growing near the middle of the front margin of the wing, are free and are used in clinging to surfaces and in crawling.

The "wings" of flying squirrels are not true wings at all, but simply unbraced folds of skin along the sides of the body, attached to the front and hind legs. Flying squirrels can sail or glide for a considerable distance by jumping from a tree and spreading this skin. The glide is usually downward, so that they alight on the trunk or branch of another tree lower than that from which they took off.

Do Bats Hibernate?

In temperate zones bats disappear as cold weather approaches, and reappear in the spring. During the winter, insect-eating bats are forced either to hibernate or migrate, since the cold weather kills the insects upon which they feed. Those that hibernate hole up in caves, hollow trees or even under loose bark. The walls of caves in some regions may be literally covered by thousands of hibernating bats hanging from some projection by their feet, heads downward. Several species make rather extensive migrations, but as yet little is known about this. It is thought that some North American bats spend the winter in Bermuda, while others apparently go to the southern United States or even farther south.

Most of the bats in the United States are active primarily at night and rest and sleep during the day in some secluded spot. Huge numbers sometimes use the same roosting quarters and emerge near dusk in hordes. One of the most famous of these nightly flights occurs at Carlsbad Caverns, New Mexico, but such flights on a smaller scale may also be seen in other regions where there are large numbers of bats.

How Blind Is a Bat?

The expression "blind as a bat" indicates a general belief that bats are either totally blind or unable to see very well. This idea probably arose because many bats avoid bright sunlight and fly primarily at dusk or night. But some bats are quite active during the day and some species, like the fruit bats or flying foxes, sleep at night and do practically all their foraging by daylight. Actually, even the night-flying species have excellent eyesight in semidarkness and can see reasonably well in broad daylight. I have occasionally seen bats flying during the day, and they obviously could see where they were going. I have also seen large numbers emerge from their roosting quarters while the sun was still bright, and at least one daylight migratory flight of many individuals has been observed.

Do Bats Get in Your Hair?

Firmly entrenched in the average woman's mind is the belief that all bats spend their time planning how they may get into the hair of the human female.

Although I have been in caves where hundreds of bats were flying about and although on some occasions my wife and other women were present, I have never seen a bat get in anyone's hair. Nor have I ever heard a reliable report of such an occurrence. While it might be possible for a bat to entangle itself in a woman's hair by accident, only a very stupid bat would do so deliberately. Nothing could snare the creature more effectively, thus putting it at the mercy of its outraged victim. It cannot be stated positively that no bat has ever gotten in any woman's hair, but if the mishap ever occurred it was by merest chance, and not a carefully planned attack on the part of the bat.

Bats Have Always Used Radar

Naturalists have known for a long time that bats can fly in total darkness without bumping into obstructions. Even before 1800 a biologist named Spallanzani reported that bats liberated in a dark room did not strike strings which he had strung across the room.

Various theories have been advanced to explain this ability, but only recently has the secret been partially solved. Blindfolded bats fly in the dark as well as those with unobstructed sight, but bats whose ears have been covered constantly bump into obstructions. It has been discovered that as bats fly they continuously emit cries that cannot be heard by human beings. These sounds are not the same as the irritated squeakings of a disturbed or captured bat, which are quite within the range of human hearing. The theory is that the inaudible or supersonic cries are reflected back to the bats and aid them in locating objects, which they are thus enabled to avoid. This principle is somewhat like that used by blind people, who avoid objects by tapping a cane and using the echo as a guide. It is said that radar operates in a similar manner. The words *echolocate* and *echolocation* have been proposed as descriptive terms for this method of locating obstacles by echoes. It is really not surprising that a bat, or for that matter any animal, is able to make and hear sounds that man cannot hear, for the range of hearing in human beings is quite different from that of many animals.

Do Vampire Bats Exist?

The vampire legend probably originated in eastern Europe long before the existence of a blood-eating bat was known. As originally described, a vampire was the restless soul of a dead person, which at night assumed one of several animal forms and stalked the countryside in search of a victim from which to suck the blood.

The bat was not associated with the vampire story until the early eighteenth century, for the very good reason that there are no European bats that feed on blood. The early explorers in South and Central America, however, encountered bats that did feed on blood, and their experiences, doubtless exaggerated, at last furnished a tangible basis for the amorphous vampire legend. Consequently, around 1725, a rash of vampire stories broke out in Europe, and since that time vampires have been thought of chiefly as bats. As far as the movies are concerned, vampires cannot exist without a whole host of bats for decoration.

There are several species of blood-eating bats to which the term vampire bat has been applied. So far as is known, bats of this type are found only in Central and South America. The largest species has a wing spread of some twelve or thirteen inches and a body length of about four inches. The weapons of the vampire bat are its modified, needle-sharp, front or incisor teeth, with which it makes small cuts in the skin of its victim. It does not suck the flowing blood, as formerly thought, but laps it up with its tongue as a cat laps milk. The bats feed upon a variety of animals including horses, cows, goats and chickens, and sometimes human beings. But they are not more partial to man than to other animals. For some unknown reason, however, they do exhibit preference for certain individuals, both human and animal. Thus, even though a number of men or animals may be available, the bats frequently attack only one or a few out of a group, night after night.

Very few people are awakened by the feeding of the bats, and the first indication that one has served as a meal for one of these winged leeches is usually the discovery of a bloodstained sheet in the morning. Possibly the saliva of the vampire bat contains something that deadens the pain of the wound; it probably does contain some substance that prevents the blood from clotting for, small as it is, the wound frequently continues to bleed for some time after the bat has stopped feeding. The vampire bat does not hover over its victim, and neither does it fan him to sleep with its wings. It may alight directly upon the body, or it may stop a short distance away and crawl up.

In some parts of South America the goats, horses, cows and chickens are so frequently attacked by vampire bats that it is almost impossible to raise them profitably. The bats also transmit diseases that kill large numbers of horses and cattle. One of the worst is the frequently fatal paralytic rabies, which has occasionally been transmitted to human beings.

How Does the Beaver Use Its Tail?

The ways in which a beaver is popularly believed to use its tail are many and various. It is generally thought, for instance, that it carries mud on its tail, and also uses it as a plasterer's trowel; that the tail serves as a prop when the beaver is gnawing a tree or waddling about on its hind legs; and further that it warns other beavers of impending danger by striking the water resoundingly with its tail.

As a matter of unadorned fact, no one has ever seen a beaver carrying mud on its tail or using it as a trowel. The mud for its lodge is carried in the beaver's front paws, with which it is also applied.

The other tail stories are true. A beaver, when alarmed, will smack its tail against the water with a resulting report so loud that every other beaver in the vicinity can hear it and dive under water to safety. While gnawing a tree, a beaver usually squats on its hind legs, propping itself with its tail. It also uses its tail for support when, its front paws full of mud, it has to walk on its hind legs.

The broad naked tail of the beaver is a positive mark of identification. The tail of the muskrat, a smaller but similar water-inhabiting animal, is slenderer and flattened from side to side.

Do Trees Cut by Beavers Always Fall Toward the Water?

Beavers use the bark of trees for food, and they use logs and branches for the construction of their dams and lodges. In their necessarily extensive tree-felling operations, they have gained the reputation of cutting trees so that they always fall toward the water, thus saving the supposedly intelligent beavers considerable effort in hauling the logs. However, most of the trees along the bank of a stream or lake have a tendency to lean toward the water, and will fall toward the water no matter what the beavers' desires are in the matter. But trees growing some distance from the water are straighter and when cut down by beavers will fall in any direction.

Can a Porcupine Shoot Its Quills?

It is commonly believed that the porcupine can purposely shoot its quills, puncturing the skin of any creature that even approaches it. When a porcupine lashes its tail at an enemy, some loose spines may become detached and be thrown a short distance; under exceptional circumstances, they may even stick into an animal. The story of the porcupine's quill-shooting ability is probably based on such rare occurrences, but ordinarily it cannot harm

[46]

anything that stays beyond reach. It is not capable of deliberately throwing or shooting its quills.

Nevertheless, its quills serve the porcupine as excellent defensive armor against the mountain lions, lynxes and other animals that sometimes prey on it. Some of these animals have been killed and have been found to have so many quills in their mouths and throats that they were probably unable to eat. The fisher, a relative of the weasel, is one of the few animals that have solved the porcupine's defense. It calmly turns the porcupine over on its back and quickly slits the unprotected belly with its sharp claws.

How Do Porcupines Mate?

Because the belly of the porcupine is relatively free of spines, considerable curiosity and a number of weird surmises have been expressed regarding the mating habits of the animals. Actually, porcupines mate as do other mammals without quills. Fortunately for the male porcupine, the female can control the spines and, during mating, pulls them tightly against its body. Of course, the female must be entirely co-operative for the process to be successful, and most males seem to have learned this, or perhaps they are born with that instinctive knowledge. Whatever the case, the females are the aggressors during the mating season, while the males continue on their stolid grunting ways until approached by an ardent female.

Are Porcupines Born Headfirst?

The fact that porcupines have quills when they are born has led to the supposition that they must always be born headfirst to prevent injury to the mother. However, the position during birth makes no difference, for the young at birth are surrounded by a relatively tough membrane that protects the female from injury. There is likewise a birth membrane around the young of most other mammals.

Chemical Warfare—The Skunk

Skunks, or polecats or wood pussies, as they are sometimes called, are best known because of their ability to emit one of the most malodorous secretions in the entire animal kingdom. This secretion is released by two glands, one on each side of the digestive tract. Ducts lead from the scent glands into the digestive tract close to its outside opening.

When the skunk gets ready to discharge its secretion, it turns its back toward the object of its wrath, raises its tail, and stamps its front feet in warning. They are sometimes quite hesitant to discharge the fluid, and it has been suggested that the stuff smells horrible even to a skunk. If warnings do not suffice, however, muscles contract and squeeze the scent glands, and the skunk lays down a barrage of spray which may be thrown for ten feet, sometimes with disconcerting accuracy. Although a relatively small amount of material is released at each discharge, usually only two or three drops if it is concentrated, it is so powerful that it can be smelled for more than half a mile in all directions.

How Not to Capture a Skunk

It is claimed that one safe way to capture a skunk is to sneak up behind it, seize it suddenly by the tail, and hoist it triumphantly into the air. A skunk held in this

Mammals

position is reportedly unable to discharge its secretion, and apparently this method of capture has succeeded in some instances. But success cannot be guaranteed, as some people have learned. Probably skunks vary in their ability to discharge their secretion when held by their tails, or possibly those that have been caught safely in this way were not in a spraying mood. At any rate, this method of capture is not recommended unless one is fully prepared to take the consequences of possible failure.

Do Migrating Lemmings Swim Out to Sea?

Lemmings are small mouselike rodents which live in most arctic and subarctic regions of the world. In Norway and adjacent areas enormous numbers of them make periodic migrations, eating everything edible in their path. According to the usual story, the migrations always end with the lemmings' plunging into the ocean and swimming out to sea.

There is considerable truth in many of the stories that are told about lemmings. Every three or four years when the feeding grounds become overpopulated by rapid reproduction, the lemmings boil out of the mountains in untold numbers and overrun the countryside. They tend to travel downhill, and the topography of Norway is such that a downhill direction eventually leads to the coast. During their migrations, they follow a rather direct route, and if streams or lakes lie across their path they attempt to swim rather than make a detour. Many, of course, are drowned; others die of a disease called lemming fever; and they are preyed upon by all kinds of animals such as foxes, bears, hawks, owls, and even reindeer. Sometimes the total loss of life is so great that only a handful or none ever reach the ocean. If they gain the coast, however, they frequently do plunge into the ocean and swim out to sea. Sometimes enough of them survive to cause consternation in all observers. In 1868 a steamer in Trondheim Fjord off the Norwegian coast encountered a swimming legion so large that fifteen minutes were required for the steamer to pass.

The reasons for many of their actions are not well understood. The final and fatal plunge into the ocean has been interpreted as a result of bad judgment on the part of the migrating hordes. It is possible that the lemmings believe the ocean is simply another small stream or lake to be quickly overcome, but this, of course, can be only a guess.

Is the Groundhog a Good Weather Prophet?

The groundhog, or woodchuck or marmot, is the most famous weather prophet in the United States. It hibernates in a burrow during the winter months and, according to tradition, emerges from hibernation on the second day of February, which for this reason has been designated groundhog day. Once out of its burrow, the groundhog casts a knowing eye over the landscape. If the day is cloudy so that it cannot see its shadow, it stays out, and the general public heaves a sigh of relief: the weather will be mild for the rest of the winter. But if the day is clear and the groundhog sees its shadow, back it pops into its burrow for more sleep, since, according to the story, this weatherwise animal knows that there will be six additional weeks of cold weather.

This is one of our oldest and quaintest traditions, but

the chances are that very few people actually believe it despite the furor and publicity attached to groundhog day. It does furnish an interesting topic of conversation for a week or so each year, and it seems almost unbecoming to examine it with the cold eye of science. Aside from the groundhog's questionable ability to predict the weather, the best reason for not believing the story is that the time of the animal's emergence from hibernation varies from year to year and probably seldom occurs on February 2. During cold weather these animals sensibly refuse to come out of their burrows, even though they are eagerly awaited by their public. Several times in the east, newsmen have been forced to disturb the sleep of some poor woodchuck in a zoological park in order to take pictures for groundhog day. But despite all scientific logic the groundhog tradition is here to stay, and newspapers doubtless will continue to feature groundhog stories from time to time.

In parts of Europe, the hedgehog, an animal similar in habits to the groundhog, is supposed to be the champion weather prophet. It is thought that the hedgehog tradition was brought from Europe by the Pilgrim Fathers, who transferred their attentions to the groundhog when no convenient hedgehog could be found.

The creature is a medium-sized rodent, a foot and a half or two feet long with a weight of about eight pounds. It is related to the ground squirrel and prairie dog and is widely distributed over the eastern half of the United States. Related species occur farther west.

Do Raccoons Wash Their Food?

Raccoons, it is often said, wash all their food before eating it, and there is some truth in this story. If water is available, most raccoons do wash their food, and some have been known actually to refuse food when they could not find any water. But refusal is not the rule; if a coon comes upon food some distance from water, he will usually eat it, though he may be unhappy about it. This washing habit is not always practiced even when it is possible; some men who have studied the habits of raccoons have never observed it.

The reason for the raccoon's peculiar action is not known. It does not indicate cleanliness, since the water used in washing the food may be dirtier than the food. Also, frogs, crawfish and similar tidbits caught in the water may be scrubbed as efficiently as other types of food. Some people believe that the raccoon washes its food because it enjoys feeling the food in the water; if this is true, it would explain why the animal sometimes almost wears the food out in its enthusiasm. A piece of meat, for instance, is sometimes mauled and scrubbed so thoroughly that it is an unrecognizable mass by the time the raccoon is ready to eat it. Whatever its reasons, however, it seems to derive considerable pleasure from the procedure.

What Mammal Has a Poisonous Bite?

One of the most interesting biological discoveries within recent years was that a certain kind of shrew, a small, mouselike animal, has a poisonous bite. An amusing sidelight on the whole affair is that many laymen already knew that some shrews have a poisonous bite, whereas biologists who took the trouble to consider the matter were sure that their bites are harmless. The results of experiments show conclusively that this time the laymen were right, and it will be surprising if the shrew population is not shortly depleted by biologists eager to test all species they can lay hands on.

The shrew whose bite has been definitely established as poisonous is the short-tailed American species, which is found throughout the eastern part of North America. Extracts prepared from the shrew's salivary glands and injected into rabbits and mice caused death within a short while, and mice bitten by the creature showed marked effects and remained in a depressed condition for some time. The venomous bite of the short-tailed shrew probably helps it to overcome the mice and other small rodents upon which it feeds. It appears quite possible that other small animals will also be found to have a poisonous bite, especially some of the European shrews whose bites are popularly thought to be poisonous.

What Is the Tallest Animal in the World?

The giraffe, thanks to its extremely long neck, is the tallest living mammal. It is possible that a few individuals twenty feet in height may exist, but the greatest height I have found recorded is eighteen feet eleven and one-half inches to the tips of the horns. Perhaps surprisingly, the giraffe has only seven bones in its neck, the same number that most other mammals have. Seen in a mounted skeleton, they remind one of sticks of stove wood stacked end to end.

Although the giraffe is the tallest mammal alive today, at least one extinct species was taller—a type of rhinoceros, *Baluchitherium* by name, remains of which have been unearthed in Mongolia. Specimens of this old fellow reached a shoulder height of seventeen feet nine inches, as opposed to ten or eleven feet for the giraffe. Added to this height at the shoulder, the giraffe has a columnar neck of some seven or eight feet, but our rhinoceros friend had a neck at least this long. In a tallest animal contest, it is believed that "Balucky" could have surpassed any living giraffe by several feet. A large specimen of the extinct rhinoceros would probably have measured nearly twenty-five feet from the soles of its front feet to the crown of its head.

Why Are Hogs Immune to Poisonous Snakes?

It is sometimes said that hogs are not harmed by the bites of poisonous snakes, and this is more or less true. Strictly speaking, hogs are not immune to snake venom, but they have something that is almost as good as immunity—a thick layer of fat just beneath the skin. The venom is probably deposited in this layer and absorbed so slowly that no harm results.

The hedgehog, however, does appear to have actual immunity to the bites of some snakes. It has been known to kill and eat the venomous European adder without suffering any ill effects if bitten during the process. But immunity is not the only weapon at its disposal. Observers have seen a hedgehog cautiously approach a snake, make a sudden snap and then quickly turn its back. The snake, if it is still able to move, usually responds by striking fiercely, only to find that its bite falls harmlessly and unpleasantly upon the hedgehog's sharp quills.

Mammals

What Are Madstones?

Madstones, snakestones and bezoars are pebbles, used as amulets, which were formerly thought to have great medicinal value; even today they are in much demand for this reason in parts of the Far East. Some writers use the terms madstone, snakestone, and bezoar synonymously, but in the United States "madstone" is preferred, while in the Far East "bezoar" is more popular. The name "snakestone" comes from a common belief that the stones are found in the heads of snakes; they have also been reported discovered in the heads of deer, toads and other animals. There is, however, no evidence that they are normally present in the head of any animal. Differing in size, shape and color, they may be round or oblong, as large as a small peach or an inch or so long, and white, black or brown.

Some of these fabulous pebbles have become quite famous in the past, and one of them is said to have been the amulet or charm described by Sir Walter Scott in his novel, *The Talisman*. Many of the stones have been in the same family for generations and consequently their origin is uncertain. However, it is likely that most of them were originally obtained from the stomachs and intestines of animals. A foreign substance sometimes gains access to the digestive tract and lodges in the stomach where eventually, in goats, antelopes, deer and related forms, it is formed by accretion into a stone. Simple balls of hair found within the stomachs of these animals, as well as genuine stones and concretions, are also frequently called madstones and bezoars.

As far as oriental medicine is concerned, the most prized

bezoars are obtained from the Persian wild goat, although those from the South American llama and the chamois are also considered useful.

As the name implies, madstones were formerly believed to be particularly effective in treating mad dog bites, although they were also supposed to be efficacious in the treatment of snakebite. The stone was placed upon the wound and allowed to remain until it dropped off of its own accord, by which time all venom or other harmful matter had supposedly been drawn from the body of the patient. The stone was then soaked in warm water or milk to remove the poison, and there have been reports that during the soaking process a greenish scum would form on the surface.

There is no scientific evidence that these stones or balls of hair have any medicinal value.

What Is the Fastest Mammal in the World?

Most authorities are agreed that for short distances the cheetah or hunting leopard is the fastest animal on feet, but its endurance is not very great. Men have used the creature for hunting gazelles and antelopes, and it usually overhauls even these swift runners with remarkable ease. But the endurance of some of the gazelles and antelopes at high speed is remarkable, and it is certain that for distances of over a mile or so either the blackbuck of India, the Mongolian gazelle, or the pronghorn antelope of the United States could outdistance any living mammal. The pronghorn antelope is easily the fastest animal in North America.

Mammals

Some writers are apparently quite pleased with man's running ability as compared to that of other animals, but I find it difficult to share this complacency. To prove man's superiority they cite cases of trained athletes who have beaten horses for a short distance. Yet what chance would a trained athlete have against a horse without a rider, and how many untrained human beings could outdistance

even a draft horse? The claim that man is one of the fastest of animals is, of course, true, but the statement is somewhat misleading. The comparison includes all species that belong to the animal kingdom, and even the slowest of us could probably outdistance a snail or even such a speedy animal as the earthworm. But reference to the following table will show that man at his fastest is quite slow indeed when compared with the really speedy members of the mammalian clan.

KNOWN RUNNING SPEED OF SOME MAMMALS

Species	Known Possible Speed; Miles per Hour	Remarks
Cheetah or hunting leopard	70	This animal has been timed at this speed with a stopwatch.
Blackbuck	65	
Mongolian gazelle	60	These animals can maintain this speed for a mile or so after which they drop to slower speeds.
Pronghorn antelope	60	When chased by a car, these animals have maintained this speed for 2 miles, and have averaged 36 MPH for 27 miles.
Gazelles (several species)	50	
Lion	50	This speed is possible for only short distances in charges after game.
Deer (several species)	45 to 50	A buck deer was timed by automobile at 49 MPH, but one biologist doubts the accuracy of the speedometer and indicates that he considers about 30 MPH the maximum for deer.
Race horse	45 to 50	

Mammals

Species	Known Possible Speed; Miles per Hour	Remarks
Jack rabbits (several species)	40 to 45	
Coyote	35 to 45	One coyote was timed for a short distance at 43 MPH. This speed seems somewhat excessive, and I do not know whether or not the speedometer was checked for accuracy.
Greyhounds and whippets	35 to 40	Whippets have been clocked with stop watches at 35.5 MPH and greyhounds at 36.
Bison	32 to 35	One of these animals has been timed with a speedometer at 32 MPH.
Grizzly bear	30 to 35	A specimen chased by a car attained 30 MPH.
Rhinoceros	25 to 28	This speed is possible for only a short distance.
Elephant	25	One African elephant has been timed with a stop watch at 24 MPH for 120 yards.
Man	22 to 25	The average speed of 22.2 MPH has been reached for the 220 yard dash, the race in which the highest average speed is attained.

Known Running Speed of Some Mammals

The foregoing table lists a few of the fastest mammals for which actual records have been made, or for which we have estimates by competent observers. The species are arranged in order of known possible speeds, but when more information is available the order may well have to be rearranged. Some animals place high in the table because of one or more speed records they have made for short distances. No figures are available for some species, which may be able to run faster for short distances than others that are higher in the table.

High Jumpers and Broad Jumpers

Obtaining accurate records for the jumping ability of most animals is quite difficult, since, aside from man, few animals vie with each other in this type of physical labor for the mere pleasure of winning. The figures given in the following table do not necessarily represent the maximum possible jump for the species concerned, but rather the approximate distances which one or more of the species have been known to jump, either by actual measurement, or by estimates of competent observers. It is unfortunate that records of this type are so incomplete.

Some mammals not included in the table and on which I have not seen any data are probably excellent jumpers. The well-trained hunting horse is said to jump between thirty-three and thirty-seven feet when it has to clear a fence or ditch, but I have not confirmed these figures to my entire satisfaction.

The possible twenty-five foot vertical jump of the klipspringer is the figure in the table most deserving of consideration. Mrs. Carl Akeley and some companions made observations upon two of these animals for several days. A female and a youngster about two-thirds grown were seen to attain the top of a rocky pedestal the sides of which sloped outward from the bottom to the top. The only possible way that the animals could have gained

access to the top was from the ground, twenty-five feet below. The observers were so located that they could see the animals as they landed on top, but they could not see the complete jump. Dr. A. Brazier Howell of the Johns Hopkins University has made a study of the running speed and jumping ability of mammals. He regards this performance of the klipspringers as most remarkable, but points out that since the complete jump was not seen, the possibility that the jump was made at a single leap can be accepted only provisionally. Klipspringers are well known for their ability to scramble up almost perpendicular cliffs, using very small projections as footholds. In this case an unnoticed intermediate foothold may have been used. At any rate, I would put my money on the klip-springer against all comers in a high-jumping contest.

It is needless to point out that the world record jumps for man are considerably in excess of those that could be made by the average person. Even many trained athletes would have difficulty in approaching these figures, while the floundering efforts of untrained human beings can well be imagined.

THE JUMPING ABILITY OF A FEW MAMMALS

Species	Probable Distance Animal Can Jump in Feet		Remarks
	Horizontal	*Vertical*	
Deer		8 to 10	Deer have been known to jump fences 8 feet high from a standing start.
Elk		8 to 10	The elk can easily clear an 8-foot fence, and could probably do considerably better than this.
Impala or pala (A type of gazelle found in Africa)	30 to 40	8 to 10	Actual measurements of close to 30 feet for a horizontal jump are recorded, and it is be-

Mammals

THE JUMPING ABILITY OF A FEW MAMMALS—*Continued*

| Species | Probable Distance Animal Can Jump in Feet | | Remarks |
	Horizontal	*Vertical*	
			lieved that the 40-foot mark may be frequently reached.
Jack rabbits (several species)	23 to 25		One antelope jack rabbit made a measured jump of 23 feet 4 inches when shot.
Jerboa pouched mice	6 to 7		An Australian animal resembling rats and mice, but possessing very elongated legs and a pouch for carrying the young.
Jerboas	12 to 15	3 to 4	Ratlike rodents with elongated hind legs, found principally in Africa. The body is 4 to 5 inches long.
Kangaroos (large species)	25 to 30	9 to 10	Individual kangaroos which were being pursued have been known to jump a fence 9 feet in height.
Kangaroo mice or jumping mice	8 to 10		These rodents possess elongated hind legs, and a body length of about 3 inches. They occur in Canada and

[63]

THE JUMPING ABILITY OF A FEW MAMMALS—*Continued*

Species	Probable Distance Animal Can Jump in Feet		Remarks
	Horizontal	*Vertical*	
			the northern United States.
Kangaroo or pocket rats	9 to 12		These rats have a body length of 4 to 5 inches and are found in western and southwestern United States.
Klipspringer		25?	A small antelope found in most mountainous areas of Africa. Stands about 20 inches at the shoulder and weighs some 40 pounds.
Leopard		8 to 10	Leopards have been reported as jumping to a rock 10 feet high while carrying prey weighing ¾ as much as themselves.
Lion		8 to 10	Lions are reported to have cleared thorn fences 6 to 7 feet high carrying prey almost as heavy as themselves. This feat has been doubted by some biologists.

Mammals

Species	Probable Distance Animal Can Jump in Feet		Remarks
	Horizontal	Vertical	
Man	26 ft.8¼ in.	6 ft. 11 in.	These figures are the official world's records as of 1947.
Rat kangaroos		8	These creatures belong to the same group as the larger kangaroos, but are much smaller.

What Animals' Teeth Never Stop Growing?

In man and many other mammals, the roots of the teeth close after the teeth have attained a certain size, so that all growth ceases. But in a number of animals, including rodents, walruses, elephants and wild boars, some of the teeth remain open at the roots; new material is added and the teeth continue to grow throughout life.

For such animals as rodents, this continuous growth is usually quite advantageous, since it prevents their teeth from being entirely worn away by their ceaseless gnawing activities. Occasionally, however, one of the teeth may grow crooked, or the lower jaw may become slightly displaced so that some of the teeth are not used and thus not worn away. But they still continue to grow. The lower teeth may curve over the snout or head and eventually make it impossible for the animal to open its mouth; or they may actually grow through the upper jaw and penetrate the

[65]

brain. I once saw the skull of a rodent, probably a ground-hog, in which that condition had developed. One of the lower incisor teeth had pierced the upper jaw, grown through it for about half an inch and emerged, continuing to grow for an inch or so before the animal died.

What Animals Have the Longest Horns?

The Indian buffalo, with a record length of approximately six and a half feet for a single horn, has produced the longest horn of any living animal. Some of the wild sheep, relatively small animals, have horns almost as long, the record length of a single one being six feet three inches.

Figures on horn spread are scarce for many species, although some horns are rated almost entirely on the basis of spread rather than length. Two species appear to be outstanding as far as present data on living animals are concerned. These are the Indian buffalo and the long-horn steer. Possibly the longhorn should not be considered, since only the steer, a result of man's "tampering with nature," produces outstanding horns. A spread of over nine feet is on record for the Indian buffalo and, although I have not seen a positively established measurement of nine feet for the longhorn steer, several such sets have been reported, and it is believed that one or more of these reports is correct.

The antlers of moose and other deer establish a different kind of record. A pair of moose antlers may weigh as much as eighty-five pounds; they are believed to be heavier and to contain more material than the horns of any other living animal.

Fights Between Some of the Larger Mammals

It is interesting for persons with sporting blood to speculate on which would win if some of the larger mammals of different species were matched in the arena. One engagement would not be conclusive, particularly if animals that had been in captivity for some time were used. Animals are at their best in the wild state and, of two contestants, the one that had suffered most in captivity would be at a decided disadvantage. Fortunately from the standpoint of this discussion, a number of fights between different species of animals have been observed, either in a sports arena or in nature. But unfortunately the details of such encounters are hard to find.

Elephant Versus Rhinoceros. Apparently a fight between these two animals was staged, or at least an attempt to stage one was made around 1500 by King Manuel of Portugal. I have found two entirely different versions of what was probably the same combat, although it is possible that two different fights were involved.

According to one writer, no fight developed. The two

[67]

animals were brought in cages into a barricaded street, one at each end. The rhinoceros showed great impatience, apparently, to be released so that it could rush over and trounce the impertinent elephant, whereas the elephant was quite calm. When the rhinoceros was released, it lowered its head and advanced toward the waiting elephant. Doubtless the spectators were watching these movements with bated breaths. Suddenly the rhinoceros must have decided that discretion was better than valor, because it turned tail and ran, bumping into the barricade in an attempt to escape. The elephant, thereupon, turned majestically and went back into its cage,

Another version simply states that the rhino won, but no details were given and I have not confirmed this outcome from other sources.

One writer describes a fight in nature between these two animals in which the rhinoceros came off a decidedly second best. The rhinoceros started the fracas by charging the elephant. The elephant calmly seized the rhinoceros around the neck with its trunk, threw it to the ground and spitted it with the tusks. The narrator did not actually see the fight, but a native who claimed to have witnessed it related the story and said that he had helped eat the carcass of the defeated rhinoceros.

Grizzly Bear Versus Lion. Two good specimens in prime condition would make an interesting match for spectators who were not squeamish. Some people believe that the grizzly would be the winner without much trouble, but I do not believe that the bear would be bored with the contest. It is said that a fight between these two animals was staged in California many years ago and that the bear won, but no details of the bout could be found.

The bear, as I have pointed out elsewhere in this book, is famous for the terrific blows it can deliver with its front paws, and the chances are that if the bear could land a good solid punch the fight would end then and there. A large grizzly outweighs a lion by a good bit, but the lion's superior agility would compensate to some extent for the difference in weight.

Grizzly Bears Versus Bulls and Bison. According to reports, it was the fashion to stage bear and bull fights in California before that state was admitted to the Union, and apparently the bear was usually the victor. As the bull charged, the bear would flick out its paw, frequently breaking the bull's neck at the first stroke, thereby with a single blow ending the fight then and there—no doubt to the disgust of the audience.

Even the great bull bison in the heyday of its existence was not safe from attack by grizzly bears. A grizzly was once seen to attack and kill four bison bulls one after the other. The first three were speedily dispatched with a single stroke for each, but the fourth was made of sterner stuff. There was a flurry of paws and horns and, although the bison was eventually killed, the bear itself was severely wounded in the encounter.

But the grizzly bear did not always emerge the victor in an encounter with a bull. J. Frank Dobie in his well known book, *The Longhorns,* tells of an instance in which a large grizzly was gored to death by an enraged longhorn. The bull was considerably the worse for wear, but he eventually recovered. No one saw the actual fight, but a short time afterward the lacerated longhorn was discovered close to

[69]

the dead grizzly, which had obviously been killed by the bloody horns of the bull.

Lion Versus Tiger. Because of the ballyhoo attached to the noble title "king of the beasts," many people are of the opinion that the lion is capable of overcoming any animal in the world. Certainly the "king" should be able to rule all members of the cat family. If we are to believe the records of the old Roman arena, however, this is not the case. During those lusty days, a lion and a tiger were frequently matched for the edification of the people of the Roman Empire, and in such a combat the tiger usually won. Most biologists who have dared to express their opinions on the subject also consider the tiger a better fighter than the lion.

There is, however, one instance on record where a circus lion killed a tiger in an adjoining cage after the two animals had broken the partition to settle their differences, but there is no record of their relative condition at the time. As I have previously indicated, all animals suffer considerably during confinement, and the one least affected would certainly have an advantage in a fight.

It is commonly believed that lions are larger than tigers, and a heavily maned lion does appear larger than a tiger of similar size. But actually the maximum known lengths and weights of tigers are greater than those of lions. The longest field measurement I have noted for a lion is ten feet eleven inches (including tail), whereas several tigers have been killed which were longer than this, the longest being eleven feet five and one-half inches. A weight of 500 pounds has been listed for a lion, but there is one of 700, one of 570 and another of 525 for tigers. The largest tiger skin known measures thirteen feet six inches (certainly stretched) as opposed to eleven feet seven inches for the lion skin. In all fairness to the dethroned king of beasts, it should be mentioned that there are more varieties of tigers than lions, and there is considerable difference in size among the groups. It is quite possible that some lions might average larger than some varieties of tigers.

Buffaloes Versus Lions and Tigers. The African and Indian buffaloes are well known for the tenacity with which they hold on to life, and for their ferocity once they are aroused. Either animal would be a formidable antagonist for practically any animal in existence.

According to reports, fights between an Indian buffalo and a tiger have been staged in India, in which the buffalo usually won by impaling the tiger with its horns. But the tiger would also get in a few choice scratches and bites of its own, so that the victor frequently had to be killed to relieve its suffering.

So far as has been determined, no one has ever seen a struggle to the death between a single lion and an African bull buffalo, but skeletons of the two animals have been found in a position that would indicate that such combats occasionally do occur, with death as a reward for both contestants. One author states that an adult bull buffalo was known to object so strenuously to serving as a meal for three lions that it successfully beat off its attackers. I have seen this or a similar instance also related in several old publications dealing with animals, and, while there is no question in my mind about the objections raised by the buffalo, there is a definite question about the final outcome. It seems probable that all these stories were based upon an experience a Major Vardon and some companions had while they were hunting in Africa many years ago; if so, the outcome of the fight was quite different. In this particular case, one of the hunters had just wounded a bull buffalo, which was in retreat when it was attacked by three lions simultaneously. There was considerable bellowing and roaring, and paws and horns flew thick and fast, but the buffalo collapsed shortly, although whether from the bullet wound or from injuries inflicted by the lions is not known. It is possible that an unwounded animal could have given a much better account of itself, and the stories in which a buffalo did successfully beat off three lions may be true. But more evidence for such an occurrence must be presented before it can be accepted unquestioningly.

Ram Versus Tiger. Sheep are usually thought of as docile and somewhat timid animals, but anyone who has had the misfortune to attract the attention of an ill-tempered ram knows that the male sheep can be a formidable antagonist. A solid butt from an angry ram has been known to discourage animals several times its size.

In parts of India, rams are bred for their fighting ability and are frequently matched for sport. One biologist tells of a man who had a fighting ram that was especially irascible; so, thinking to rid himself of the troublesome beast, he put it in a tiger's den. According to the story, the ram immediately gave the tiger a resounding butt, which apparently so stunned the cat that the ram was able to kill it.

This instance is related to illustrate how animal fights may sometimes have an unexpected end, and to emphasize the fact that a single match between different species does not allow one to form positive conclusions about their respective abilities.

Do Bulls See Red?

It is firmly ingrained in the average mind that anything red makes a bull beside itself with rage and incites it to immediate attack. No bullfight would be complete without the bright red capes which matadors flick unconcernedly under the very noses of their raging adversaries.

Biologists have recently punctured the balloon of this ancient belief, but it will be many years before all laymen accept the results of their experiments. They have proved, however, that bulls cannot distinguish red from any other color. They are, in fact, color blind. This fact is privately admitted by many bullfighters, and in some experiments matadors who used white cloths got the same reactions from the bulls as those who used red cloths. It is the movement of the cape that causes the bull to charge— not the color of it. Although the bulls cannot tell a white cape from a red one bloodthirsty human spectators at a bullfight certainly can, and the bullfighter does not exist who would have the temerity to appear in the arena with an unromantic white cape.

With the exception of man and monkeys, all other mammals upon which any work in this connection has been done have also been found to be color blind.

Do Animals' Eyes Shine in the Dark?

Many readers probably believe they know the answer to this question, since most of us have seen the glow of animals' eyes as we have driven along a highway at night.

Actually, however, the eyes themselves do not shine; the glow is merely the reflection of light from some other source, such as headlights, flashlights or campfires. It is caused by the fact that many animals have in their eyes a layer of crystalline substance which has the quality of reflecting light. Human eyes have practically none of this substance and consequently seldom shine in the dark. Since this reflecting layer is also of assistance in seeing in the dark, most animals can see better at night than can man. The slight difference in the color of the light reflected from the eyes of different animals is partly due to the different number of blood vessels in their eyes. Eyes containing many blood vessels glow with a definite red color; those with few blood vessels have a whiter glow.

Why Do Cows Chew Their Cuds?

Anyone familiar with cows knows that when they are not actively eating they are usually contentedly munching their cuds, a process that is apparently not only pleasurable, but also essential to the health of the animal.

The cow's stomach is divided into four compartments, but the statement that the cow has four complete stomachs is not true, strictly speaking. When cows eat grass or other food, they chew it only enough to enable them to swallow it. The food passes first into the front division of the stomach, called the rumen or paunch, which is simply a storage place. From the rumen, it gradually passes into the second stomach division, where it is compacted into small masses or cuds. When the cow is resting, the cuds are regurgitated one by one, thoroughly chewed and mixed with saliva. When the cow swallows the cud, it goes by way of a valve in the throat to the third division of the stomach where digestion begins. The fourth stomach division plus the intestine completes the digestive process.

Other animals that chew a cud include deer, sheep, goats, giraffes and antelopes. Animals of this type are called ruminants, because the first part of the stomach is the rumen.

Why Do Monkeys Search Their Hair?

Anyone who has watched monkeys in a zoological park has observed the industry with which they search through their own or another monkey's hair. The search seems usually to be rewarded, since frequently the hunter triumphantly pops something into his mouth.

The general supposition is that they are hunting for parasites, and there is probably some truth in the idea. However, it is thought likely that the parasites are not their only objective. Properly cared-for monkeys quickly lose the parasites they have when they are first captured, yet they search through their hair or the hair of their neighbors just as carefully and with as much apparent success as do monkeys that are still infested. Most biologists believe that captive monkeys are looking for pieces of dried skin and particles of salt exuded by the skin, although they agree that the busy little animals are not averse to any lice they may find.

What Mammals Have Four Horns?

There occurs in parts of India and Burma the only wild mammal in the world with four horns. This is the

four-horned antelope, a relatively animal that
weighs about forty pounds. Only th
and, in some cases, even they have
The rear pair, which may be four to .ength,
are the longer and grow in essentially .e position as
the horns of other mammals. The front pair are just above
the eyes, and may attain a length of two and a half inches.

Several kinds of domestic sheep have been selectively
bred and now have various numbers of horns. Perhaps the
most interesting are the unicorn or one-horned sheep and
the four-horned varieties. The unicorn sheep is found
principally in Nepal, India, and its one horn is really
two, fused together for more than half the length. In
many specimens of this breed, the horns separate toward
the end and curve independently, occasionally even sweep-
ing downward toward the neck. There has been considerable discussion about whether this peculiar horn condition
is inherited or whether each sheep is given special treatment while young to induce the horns to develop abnormally. So far as I know this question has not been settled.

The four-horned sheep are equally spectacular. In some
varieties one pair of horns grows upward and outward
more or less normally, while the second pair, behind the
first, grows outward and downward, with the points directed toward the sheep's nose.

How Does a Cat Purr?

Purring is caused by the vibration of the cat's vocal
cords. When air is taken into the lungs, it passes through
the voice box that contains the vocal cords. Purring is of
course under the control of the cat. When it wishes to

express its contentment, the vocal cords are allowed to vibrate as the air passes in and out of the lungs during breathing. When the cat is asleep, or if it does not want to purr for some reason, the passage of air does not affect the vocal cords and no purr is produced.

Does the Giraffe Have a Voice?

Giraffes are traditionally considered to be as voiceless as the proverbial clam. Hunters have said that they do not make a sound even when wounded, and until recent years even biologists believed that they were as mute as they are popularly thought to be.

Recently, however, observations of giraffes in zoological parks have shown that at least an occasional specimen is capable of making certain types of noises. Female giraffes have been heard to moo or low softly, particularly when they were concerned about the welfare of their calves, and young giraffes, when hungry, have been heard to make sounds like those of a calf. The voice box or larynx of a giraffe is comparatively undeveloped, and it is possible that only some of them can make sounds. Perhaps the voice box is better developed in the young than in the adults, for according to reports the young produce more noticeable sounds.

What Mammal Lives Longest?

Aside from man, who will not be considered in this discussion, the elephant has the reputation of being the longest-lived mammal. One frequently sees statements, credited even by some biologists, that it lives for 150 to 200 years.

The question has been investigated recently by several biologists, who have found that there is no positive record of an elephant's having lived to be one hundred years old. It has been reasonably well verified that one elephant attained an age of over sixty years, and several over fifty years of age are known. Another elephant is said to have lived in the United States for eighty-five years, but I have not been able to confirm this report. It seems probable that elephants do live about as long as any other mammal, and many authorities believe that an occasional specimen may reach one hundred years.

Comparatively little information on the maximum age of whales is yet available, but most biologists are of the opinion that they do not live so long as many other mammals. Whales have been killed whose bodies contained harpoons that were marked with the date when they were made. From this "harpoon evidence," one whale is thought to have been approximately thirty-seven years old at the time of its death.

The domestic horse probably lives as long as any other mammal with the possible exception of the elephant. Ages of from fifty-four to sixty-two years have been reported and biologists who have investigated these claims have provisionally accepted ages of over fifty years as approximately correct.

Known ages for other mammals kept in captivity include a hippopotamus of forty-one years, a rhinoceros of forty, several kinds of bears of thirty to thirty-four, a chimpanzee of twenty-six, and monkeys of over twenty years. Domestic cats and dogs have done well. Cats of twenty-one and twenty-three have been reasonably well verified, and others of twenty-seven, twenty-nine and thirty-one have been reported. Dogs of eighteen and twenty-two years are provisionally accepted, and one is reputed to have lived for thirty-four years.

One of the most amazing records for mammalian age has been established by a spiny anteater, one of the two types of mammals that lay eggs. This little animal, appropriately named "Prickley Pete," has lived and thrived in the Philadelphia Zoo for more than forty-two years and, at last report, was as lively and healthy as ever.

PART TWO
Birds

What Are Birds?

Birds are the only animals that have feathers, which makes their identification as a class a simple matter. The front limbs of all birds have become modified into wings the bones of which are not very different from those in the human arm. As in the arm, a single bone connects the wing to the body, and below the elbow there are two bones. The part of the bird's wing that corresponds to man's wrist and hand has become considerably modified, since in the bird only three fingers are represented, and two of these are usually quite small. These three bones, bound together by tissue, probably correspond to the thumb, the first or index finger and the third or middle finger of the human hand. The bones representing the first finger are usually the best developed; in some species the other two are hard to find.

What is popularly called the wishbone in a bird can be compared with the human collarbones. In man the bones are separate, but in birds they have become fused together at one end. This modification is doubtless correlated with the flight habits of birds.

[83]

Birds, like mammals, are warm blooded; their body temperature thus remains more or less constant despite the temperature of the air. As a rule, the normal temperature of birds is higher than that of mammals. If the body temperature of a man were to become as high as it is in many birds, he would have a raging fever, and if he were still alive after attaining the maximum temperature for birds he would be a medical curiosity. Normal bird temperatures range from about 100 to 112 degrees as compared with the normal of 98.6 for man.

What Birds Cannot Fly?

There are some birds that cannot fly, including the well-known ostrich and its relatives. However, with the exception of the kiwi, a peculiar New Zealand bird, even the flightless birds have fairly well-developed wings. The wings of the kiwi have been modified into mere stubs, so that it appears to be entirely wingless.

The name emu is probably more familiar to cross-word puzzle fans than the name of any other flightless bird with the exception of the ostrich. Emus are natives of Australia, but they have become rare in some areas. The male is smaller than the female, and after the eggs are laid, he incubates them and takes care of the resulting brood of chicks.

How Scarce Are Hens' Teeth?

"Scarce as hens' teeth" is an appropriate description for nonexistent objects, because teeth are entirely lacking, not only in hens, but in all birds. The lack does not seem to inconvenience them, however, since they swallow their food whole without any ill effects. This process is made possible by the gizzard, a muscular organ which substitutes for teeth and which is really part of the bird's stomach. The principal function of the gizzard is to break up the food into small particles so that it can be digested, and the birds occasionally swallow small stones that are of assistance in the process. With the gizzard, they are able to grind up even such hard food as grain and other seed.

The craw or crop as it is sometimes called, like the gizzard, is a modified part of the bird's digestive tract. It is a saclike enlargement of the food tube, or esophagus, just in front of the gizzard in the region where the neck joins the body. It is used principally for storing food, although in some birds digestion starts in this organ. A hen or other bird can rapidly gobble up large quantities of food without danger of indigestion because the food is held in the craw for a time before passing on into the gizzard. A well-filled crop is quite noticeable in young chickens and can be easily felt even in adult birds. A few birds, such as pigeons, doves and their relatives, secrete a milklike material in the craw called "pigeon's milk." This is a whitish substance that the parent bird regurgitates and feeds to its young.

Birds Have More Neckbones Than a Giraffe

The neck of a chicken is not considered choice eating by most people, but it is a part of the bird that should be looked upon with a certain amount of respect. There are more bones in the neck of any bird than in the neck of a giraffe. The number of bones varies with the kind of bird, birds with long necks usually having the greatest number.

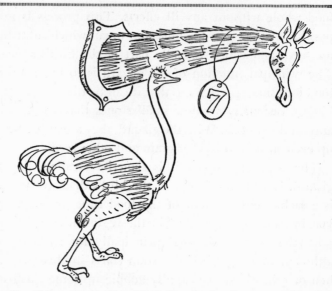

The English sparrow has fourteen, ducks sixteen and swans twenty-three. The long-necked giraffe, as I have pointed out elsewhere in this book, has but a paltry seven.

What Was the Thunderbird?

Many tribes of Indians relate tales of a gigantic eagle-like bird which many, many years ago was the scourge of the western plains. These enormous thunderbirds, as they were called, were supposed to carry off human beings and were even reported to feed upon bison. One story tells of the battle of a young Indian chief with a thunderbird that had recently seized and carried away his wife. Although a brave man, the Indian realized that a single human being armed only with bow and arrows would stand no chance against such an adversary as the thunderbird; so he decided to try to kill the bird by trickery. Consequently, he selected a group of his friends and had them conceal themselves near the thunderbird's nest. The warrior then strode forth and shouted his defiance to his enemy. The great bird swooped down to seize him and was promptly slain by a volley of arrows shot by the warrior's friends.

Such tales have been scoffed at by biologists for many years, but the recent discovery in California of the remains of an enormous eaglelike bird proves that birds of prey much larger than living species did exist in the past. The skull of this monster bird is twice the size of the bald eagle's, its other bones being also proportionately larger. It thus seems quite possible that the thunderbird legend of the western Indians was based upon a bird that actually did exist at one time and it may be that the bird also attacked human beings. However, it is doubtful that even these great birds could have carried anyone off, or that they would have been capable of killing a bison.

Was the Roc a Real Bird?

Many readers will doubtless recall the adventures of Sinbad the Sailor of Arabian Nights fame, who was carried away by a huge bird called a roc. The existence of such a bird was also supported by Marco Polo, who wrote of a legend of the natives of Madagascar. According to this story, birds of tremendous size had been seen to seize elephants in their claws, carry them, struggling, to great heights and drop them, then settle on the carcasses and eat their fill. Like the thunderbird of Indian legend, the roc was also said to prey upon human beings and domesticated animals.

There is no evidence that enormous birds of this type

ever existed, but skeletons and egg shells of a large extinct species have been found in Madagascar, which may have given rise to the story of the roc. These birds, however, could not have flown away with a field mouse, much less an elephant, for they could not fly at all. Variously called rocs, elephant birds, or giant birds, they were probably somewhat larger than ostriches, but the most remarkable thing about them was the size of their eggs. Almost complete shells of these eggs have been discovered, and some of them will hold over two gallons.

What Bird Eats Living Sheep?

Before sheep were introduced into New Zealand, the kea parrot was content to feed upon berries, fruits, seeds and similar food, and was thus a respected denizen of that country. But a short time after sheep appeared the feeding habits of many of the birds changed to include living sheep. It is said that they attack a live sheep, tear a hole in its body with their sharp beaks and eat the fat surrounding the kidneys. The sheep, of course, die as a result of such a wound. It is not definitely known why this sudden shift in diet took place, but it is thought probably that the birds first acquired a taste for flesh around slaughterhouses.

The New Zealand Government has placed a bounty on the kea parrot which has resulted in the killing of large numbers of them, but they are still numerous in some areas. Fortunately for the sheep raisers, not all the parrots will attack living sheep; nevertheless, a sufficient number have acquired the habit to have caused the abandonment of sheep ranches in some districts.

Birds

What Bird Picks the Teeth of Crocodiles?

The black-backed courser of Africa, a medium-sized bird related to the sandpipers, has earned the name of crocodile bird because of its association with crocodiles. Crocodiles have a habit of basking in the sun for long periods and frequently lie with their mouths partially open. Parts of their bodies, including the inside of their mouths, are sometimes infested with leeches, parasitic worms related to the familiar and considerably less detestable earthworms. Crocodile birds are quite fond of these leeches, and pick large numbers of them from the crocodiles' bodies. If the body pickings are slim, the bird will enter the partly open mouth of the crocodile and gobble up any leeches lurking within as well as bits of food lodged between the teeth. As soon as its meal is finished, the bird, which apparently does not put too much trust in the crocodile, flies out backward, not even taking the time to turn around. Some authorities doubt the reports of this habit, but it has been observed in at least one captive bird and is apparently accepted by most biologists who have investigated the matter.

A Bird That Walks on Water

One of the oddest sights in the bird world is a medium-sized, blackish bird apparently walking about on the surface of the water. This peculiar bird is the jaçana, a relative of the plovers. Unfortunately for anyone who would like to tell an excellent bird story, the jaçana does not actually walk on the water, although from a distance it appears to be doing just that. Really, however, it is walking on lily pads and other aquatic vegetation, which, under its weight, sink out of sight below the water surface. This still rather remarkable feat is made possible by the bird's very long toes which have a span sufficient to stretch over parts of several leaves, thus distributing the bird's weight. Examining a specimen at close range, one's eyes are continually drawn to its absurdly large feet.

Aside from its feet, the jaçana at rest does not have an especially striking appearance. Its general color is a greenish black, but if it is disturbed there is a flutter of brilliant yellowish green which was hidden when the wings were folded, and the bird is away with its long trailing toes clearly visible. A jaçana in flight should not be confused with any other species, since there is no other black bird in the American tropics with yellow wings. Most jaçanas are tropical in distribution, but one species extends as far north as southern Texas.

A Bird With Fingers on Its Wings

The bones of three fingers are represented in the wings of many birds, but in most species they are so modified that they are not usable. However, the young hoatzin, a strange South American bird, has on its wings two long free clawed digits which it uses efficiently in climbing among the branches of the trees. The nestlings are excellent swimmers long before they are able to fly. Their nests are frequently built on branches overhanging water, and the baby hoatzin, if frightened, may climb from the nest, dive into the water and remain there for a long time. When the danger is past, it climbs laboriously back to the nest using its beak, legs and the wing fingers in the process.

By the time the young bird becomes an adult, the fingers have degenerated into small knobs or protuberances.

Adult hoatzins are such weak fliers that one wonders how they are able to survive all the dangers of the South American jungle. One reason may be that their flesh, which has a very musty taste, is repellent to the other jungle animals. The birds are not eaten even by the natives, who express their contempt for the taste of the hoatzins' flesh by calling them stink birds.

A Bird That Practices Self-Mutilation

Some years ago while walking through a dense area of the Panamanian jungle, I was nearly frightened out of a year's growth by a loud squawking cry almost in my ear. When I was not immediately attacked by a ferocious man-eating animal, I gathered courage and looked around. The only living creature I could locate was a greenish bird with a reddish breast and long tail perched on a vine some thirty feet away. Again the raucous cry broke the silence, and to my sheepish surprise I saw that it came from this bird. Such was my introduction to the great rufous motmot, a bird related to the kingfishers.

Although the cry of the great rufous motmot seems oddity enough for one bird, it has another startling habit. Apparently not satisfied with the decorations given it by nature, it prefers to change its appearance by actually mutilating itself, although the consequences are not serious. The tail of the motmot is composed of several feathers, the tips of which, in the adult, are shaped like tennis rackets. This peculiar shape is the result of the bird's own actions. In young birds the tail feathers are complete, but the adults bite off all the barbs from the central shaft of the feathers an inch or so from the tips, leaving the tips themselves barbed.

What Songbird Flies Under Water?

We accept the fact that such birds as ducks, penguins, grebes and related birds are capable of swimming well and diving to considerable depths, for we know they are especially constructed for this type of activity. But it does seem strange that one of the totally unrelated songbirds—the water ouzel or dipper—should lead a similar existence. These birds, found in the western United States and in other mountainous areas of the world, feed primarily upon water insects and seem to enjoy diving into the water in search of them. Not only do they stroll about on the bottom of a swiftly flowing stream, but they frequently fly under water, using their wings as though they were in the air. The feathers of the water ouzel are so thick and tightly fitting that its body does not get wet. This feather arrangement also probably explains why cold weather does not reduce the activities of these birds. They have, for example, been seen to fly through holes in the ice and to emerge some time later none the worse for their chilly bath.

Dippers are grayish-colored birds about the size of a robin. They have noticeably short tails and somewhat resemble the thrushes to which they are related. Their name probably derives from an interesting habit which the young birds have. When they are hungry, apparently feeling that they must put on an act, either as persuasion for the parent birds to feed them or as advance payment for a meal, they execute a series of squats or dips, bending their knees, squatting down and then straightening up again.

What Birds Are the Best Talkers?

Several kinds of birds can be taught to say a few words, and some species are capable of uttering rather long sentences. These talking birds include the parrots, mynas, crows, ravens, jackdaws and some species of jays. Most authorities agree that the two champion bird talkers are the African parrot and the hill myna of India, but there is considerable debate over which is the better. Some of the other parrots from South and Central America are also very good.

Quite recently a talking starling has appeared on the scene. Caught when quite young and raised to adulthood, it shows indications of rivaling many of the other famous talkers. This is rather unusual in a starling, for while they are wonderful mimics very few have learned to talk fluently.

It has been said that the structure of the tongue is the factor that chiefly determines whether or not a bird can talk. Parrots have large thick tongues, and some people believe this is the principal reason why as a group they are rather efficient talkers. It is possible that the tongue does aid the parrot in the formation of words, but a large thick tongue is not necessary for speech, nor is it a guarantee that its possessor will be able to talk. Birds of prey have the same general type of tongue as parrots, and biologists have yet to hear of a talking hawk or eagle. The tongues of mynas, starlings and many other birds that are either good

[93]

talkers or excellent mimics are quite slender and horny. So far as is known, no one particular organ is essential to speech production; as other writers have suggested, the formation of words is probably no more difficult than is the production of song and other characteristic bird sounds.

Many people believe that splitting the tongues of crows, starlings and similar birds helps them to talk. Nothing could be further from the truth. If the tongue is split, the bird will not do nearly so well as it did before. Apparently people interpret the peculiar noises made by such mutilated birds as an attempt to form words, but actually a split-tongued bird can no longer make even the sounds characteristic of its kind, which is the reason that its cries sound so strange. Many of these birds, of course, would not be able to talk even with an unmutilated tongue, but splitting the tongue is one way to guarantee that the bird will not talk.

A still-unsettled question is whether or not birds realize the significance of the words they use. They do sometimes form definite associations between certain expressions and actions, but again they repeat sentences at most inappropriate times. Most biologists think that they do not realize the meaning of their words, but more work must be done on this point before positive statements can be made.

The Laziest Bird in the World

The cowbird and the European cuckoo are about equal contenders for the title of The World's Laziest Bird. Neither of them builds a nest in which to rear the young; each lays its eggs in the nests of other species. In many cases the owner of the nest does not notice anything amiss, and incubates the alien egg and raises the young cowbird or cuckoo as devotedly as though it were its own. The really bad aspect of the situation is that in most cases the young cowbird or cuckoo deliberately pushes the eggs or young of the rightful owner from the nest. Thus for each cowbird or cuckoo that is reared there is usually one legitimate brood of young birds that dies. There are a few species of birds, however, that discover the strange egg in their nests and appear to resent the intrusion. The yellow warbler uses a novel but difficult method of ridding itself of the cowbird egg. Instead of simply throwing the offending egg overboard, it usually builds a complete new nest over the old one containing the cowbird egg. As many as three yellow warbler nests, one above the other, have been found, the lower two holding a cowbird egg.

Cowbirds are so called because of their habit of gathering in flocks in the vicinity of cows. Depending even in their feeding upon the exertions of another animal, they catch and eat the grasshoppers and other insects that the cows flush from the grass as they graze. The male cowbird is the only black bird with a brown head in the United States; the female is a dull gray color. They are slightly larger than English sparrows.

Do Ostriches Stick Their Heads in the Sand?

One of the most prevalent beliefs about ostriches is that, when frightened, they stick their heads in the sand and feel perfectly content that they are safely hidden. When an ostrich has its head in the sand, so the story goes, a person can walk up to it and pluck its feathers, or capture it easily.

Stupid as the ostrich undoubtedly is, even the most critical authorities do not believe it is stupid enough to do anything so feeble minded as to stick its head in the sand, and no one has ever observed this action in either captive or wild birds. However, they do have an interesting habit which may have given rise to the story. When sighting possible danger from afar, ostriches sometimes drop to the ground, stretch their necks out parallel with it and watch intently. When the danger becomes imminent, however, the ostrich reacts as other animals do, it beats a hasty retreat.

Is It True That Ostriches Will Eat Anything?

Ostriches are likely to swallow practically any small or medium-sized object that is offered to them, but this does not mean that they may not be injured as a result. Being very stupid birds, or perhaps too trustful of human beings who offer them ice picks, files and other "delicacies" to eat, they cannot be relied on to judge what they can digest successfully, and many zoological parks have lost valuable birds as a result of this indiscriminate appetite.

Ostriches can survive a reasonable amount of foreign substances and, like many other birds, actually require stones and pebbles for the proper functioning of the digestive system. It may be that captive ostriches swallow the harmful object offered them because they do not get enough pebbles or the proper food in captivity. Certain it is that if wild birds ate as much indigestible material as do captive birds, the ostrich clan would shortly become extinct.

[96]

Birds

Do Sea Birds Drink Sea Water?

Sea birds are able to drink sea water without harm and in many instances prefer it to fresh. In fact, some species must have sea water to drink or they will die. Birds that have been seen drinking sea water include penguins, shearwaters and terns. Some species of penguins drink either salty or fresh water, but at least one young penguin is known to have died presumably because it drank too much fresh water.

Some physiologists have doubted whether sea birds are able to drink salt water, but they have been seen to do so so often that the fact seems well-established. It is not known how they are able to do so and still remain healthy, but obviously the ability is a distinct advantage to those birds that seldom have an opportunity to find fresh water.

Are There Penguins at the North Pole?

Penguins are found only in the areas south of the equator where, as a group, they have a fairly wide distribution. Some species are found on various South Sea Islands, in parts of Australia, New Zealand and in some parts of South America. At least one species is found as far north as the coastal regions of Peru. Auks and puffins, found in the arctic regions, greatly resemble penguins, and the two groups may be confused by people who are not biologists. Penguins are flightless, but auks and puffins are able to fly.

What Birds Have a Common Burial Ground?

One of the most persistent animal stories, chiefly heard in connection with elephants, is that some animals have community graveyards. However, though much talked about, not one was ever found until Dr. Robert Cushman Murphy, of the American Museum of Natural History, recently discovered a penguin burial ground on South Georgia Island in the antarctic. There was a large colony of penguins on the island, but Dr. Murphy noticed that there were seldom any dead birds to be found. Before leaving the island, he discovered why. One day he found a small clear lake on top of a hill some distance from the ocean. Around the edge of the lake were several droopy penguins which were obviously sick or seriously injured. Further examination revealed that the bottom of the lake was literally covered with dead penguins, the icy cold water having preserved the bodies in perfect condition. Apparently most of the seriously ill or injured birds of the colony came to this quiet spot and enjoyed a few moments of peace before consigning themselves to their watery graves.

So far as I know, this penguin graveyard is the only common burial ground of animals that has ever been discovered. I have not found a report of a similar practice among other groups of penguins.

Fledglings That Are Larger Than Their Parents

Some young birds actually shrink in the process of becoming adults. This phenomenon has been investigated in several species. The young of some swallows, for instance, have been found to be as much as twenty-five per cent larger than their parents. The characteristic is probably true of other birds also, including eagles, hawks and several of the sea birds, since the young birds appear considerably larger and heavier than the adults.

It is easy to see that such an arrangement could be an advantage. Many sea birds, such as the albatrosses and the shearwaters, feed their young until they are almost bursting with accumulated fat. When the young birds have completed their growth, the parents fly away over the ocean, leaving the fledglings to shift for themselves. The layers of stored-up fat are now of prime importance, since the sudden shift from dependence to enforced independence is quite drastic. By the time the young birds have learned the tricks of obtaining food and of flying, they have used up most of the reserve food supply in their bodies and are approximately the size of their parents.

Do Eagles Carry Off Young Children?

Most of the stories about attacks by eagles and other birds of prey upon human beings raise two separate though related questions. Do birds of prey carry off young children? Will they make unprovoked attacks upon human beings?

All the accounts that I have seen of young children who were carried away by these birds date back many years. Thus we read of a bearded vulture's attacking a three-year-old child in Switzerland in 1763 and carrying it for half a mile before the bird was discovered and driven away. Some years later, a white-tailed sea eagle was reported to have carried a child to its nest and killed it before the rescue party arrived. This happened in the Faroe Islands, north of the British Isles, and was supposed to have been well verified.

One of the important factors to be considered in determining the truth of such stories is the weight which it is known these birds are able to carry. The golden eagle can fly with a weight of seven or eight pounds, and it is not thought that even larger species can carry over fifteen or sixteen pounds. The feet of condors, the largest birds of prey, are relatively weak, so that they are not capable of carrying as heavy a load in their claws as are some of the eagles. It therefore seems impossible that any bird of prey could fly with any child except a very young infant. Despite many supposedly authentic stories, I do not believe that there is a single verified case. However, I see no reason why, in remote areas where the birds have not learned to fear man, they might not attack and carry off a very small unguarded baby just as they would attack a rabbit or other animal. In most regions, however, the birds are afraid of man and the chances are therefore very much against such an occurrence.

There have been several relatively recent reports of eagles making unprovoked attacks on human beings, and some of them at least appear to be well authenticated. In one case, reportedly investigated by Edward H. Forbush, an ornithologist, a golden eagle attacked a nine-year-old girl. Fortunately, her parents were near, rushed to the rescue, and killed the bird with some difficulty. The girl suffered lacerations and bruises. In another case reported from Scotland, a golden eagle, which earlier in the day had missed a meal when the bird it was pursuing fell exhausted at the feet of a hunter, some time later attacked the hunter. Before the man knew what was happening, the eagle had fastened its claws in his ankle. It hung on grimly, and the man would probably have been seriously injured had not his dog attacked the eagle. As it was, the bird was killed only after a considerable fight, and even then its talons had to be cut from the man's leg.

I see no reason to doubt these stories. Eagles, condors and vultures have been known to kill even such large active animals as sheep, antelopes and coyotes, eating them on the spot and making no attempt to carry them away. Birds of prey that have not learned to fear man might as readily attack a human being as some other animal.

How Do Buzzards Find Dead Animals?

There has been considerable argument over whether sight or smell is more important to buzzards in locating dead animals, and even today the question is not entirely settled. A rather crude experiment which I tried when I was a boy may prove of interest. A friend and I had been hunting very unsuccessfully for several hours and we sat down to rest for a time. We had recently heard a discussion of this question, and we decided to try to attract some buzzards by using our bodies for bait. These birds were numerous in the general area, but since none were in sight at that time we lay down in an open field near some trees and remained motionless. Within a few minutes a turkey buzzard sailed into view, and it was very shortly joined by several others. After circling for a time, the birds settled in the nearby trees and peered hungrily at our bodies. After many more hopeful birds joined the waiting throng, we became tired of the experiment, got to our feet and resumed the hunt. There was a great beating of wings as the buzzards flapped off in disgust to look for more fertile fields. In this particular case, it is fervently hoped that the sense of sight was the most important in the locating of the bodies!

Other investigators have discovered, however, that the birds have found bodies of animals that were completely covered, and in a few cases buzzards have found animal carcasses within a short time after they had been placed out at night. These actions seem to show that the sense of smell was involved more than the sense of sight. It seems quite probable that both sight and smell may be used, and that the relative importance depends upon the situation. I personally believe that sight is the most important for the location of food at great distances, but that the sense of smell probably functions in finding putrefying carcasses that are concealed from view.

What Bird Kills Rattlesnakes?

The road runner, one of the most familiar birds of the southwestern and western United States, takes its name from its habit of running along the road in front of wagons or any other slow vehicle. Other names for this picturesque bird are chaparral bird, ground cuckoo and snake eater.

Many stories have been told about the road runner's relations with rattlesnakes. Perhaps the most common is that it will build a corral of cactus or other spiny twigs about a sleeping rattlesnake, then attack the snake and kill it. Road runners have been seen to attack, kill and even eat rattlesnakes, but no biologist has ever seen one build a corral about a rattlesnake, and until such confirmation is available this amusing notion cannot be accepted.

When a road runner fights a rattlesnake, it first fluffs its feathers, unfolds its wings, then attacks. The snake strikes at the bird repeatedly, but its bites fall harmlessly upon the bird's extended wing feathers. The fight usually ends when a well-aimed peck by the bird finds a vital spot on the snake's head. One road runner was seen to kill a rattlesnake three and a half feet long, after which it ate the snake's brain and nothing else. A snake over a foot or so in length is too large to be swallowed completely; the bird simply swallows as much as possible and waits until it has been digested before swallowing more. While waiting, the road runner walks about unconcernedly with part of the snake dangling from its mouth.

The Dodo Was a Real Bird

Most everyone knows the meaning of the expression "dead as a dodo," but many people do not realize that the bird was once very much alive. A peculiar, clumsy, flightless bird about the size of a turkey, it was first discovered in 1507 on the island of Mauritius off the western coast of Madagascar. Sailors used them for food, killing them with such ease that they called the birds "doudos" or stupid. Today, the term dodo is frequently applied to stupid people. Dogs, rats, pigs and people killed the young birds indiscriminately and ate the eggs, with the result that less than 200 years after their discovery the dodos were extinct. The few restorations in various museums are not based on living specimens, but were made long after the last bird was dead. It is thus possible that the real dodo was somewhat less ridiculous in appearance than the restorations would lead us to believe.

How Did the Passenger Pigeon Become Extinct?

Sixty or seventy years ago there were probably more passenger pigeons in the United States than any other single species of bird. Today, not a single living specimen remains. The last wild bird was seen in 1906. The last one in captivity was "Martha," a female hatched at the Cincinnati Zoo where she lived to the ripe old age of twenty-six. When it grew apparent that the passenger pigeon was rapidly becoming extinct, the Zoo made efforts to save the species and offered large rewards for a male, but without results. Efforts to cross the female with other species also failed, and on September 1, 1914, Martha died, the last representative of a once numerous race. Fortunately, Martha was not tossed into an ash can, as are many dead birds. She was mounted and is now on exhibition at the Smithsonian Institution in Washington, D. C.

This pigeon, larger than the common mourning dove but similar in general appearance, ranged at one time over most of the eastern part of the North American continent. The birds flew in huge flocks in numbers beyond comprehension. Some of the flocks were estimated to contain between one and two billion birds; when they were on the move, they literally hid the sun. Unfortunately, they nested in great colonies, a habit probably more responsible for their extinction than any other one factor. The birds were a popular food, and their nesting areas were raided and the young and adults killed and shipped by the carloads. When the food markets became glutted, the birds were fed to hogs or were used for fertilizer. Even countless millions could not withstand this ruthless slaughter. Today a few unexciting specimens, peering vacantly through glass eyes from museum cases, are all that remain of the passenger pigeon.

What Is an Egg?

The egg of any bird is a more complicated production than superficial consideration would lead us to believe. The yellow or yolk of the egg is formed within the bird's reproductive organ or ovary. The yellow breaks out of the ovary, enters the upper end of the reproductive tract or oviduct, where the white is added; then travels down to the lower part of the tube where the membranes and shell are applied around the yellow and white. The egg then is ready to be laid—an accomplishment that the hen announces to the world with loud cacklings.

Only a small part of the egg is living material that will develop into a young bird or chicken. This is the small whitish spot in the yellow, which can easily be seen if a hen's egg is removed from the shell. During incubation the young chicken or bird is formed from the small living part of the egg, while the yolk and white serve as food material for the developing embryo. In fertilized eggs—and most eggs are fertilized unless roosters and hens are separated—a certain amount of development occurs before the egg is laid. Therefore, when one breakfasts upon a platter of eggs, one is in reality eating embryonic chickens.

What Makes Double Eggs?

Hens sometimes lay what is called a double egg, a large egg containing two yolks. The method of formation of the most common type of double egg is relatively simple. As a usual thing, only one yellow is discharged from the ovary at a time, the next one being released a day or so later. Sometimes, however, two yolks are liberated at once and pass down the reproductive tract very close together. The white, membranes and shell are applied around both yellows, thus forming a double egg.

Sometimes a complete egg with a shell is found within another shell which also contains a white and yolk. An egg of this kind may be formed in one of several ways, as has been pointed out by Dr. J. T. Patterson of the University of Texas and other workers. In one method of formation, it is thought that one yellow is discharged from the ovary as usual and passes down the egg tube where white, membranes and shell are applied to the outside. Then, instead of discharging the egg in the normal way, the reproductive tube goes into reverse and carries the fully formed egg back to the upper end near the ovary. By the time the egg has reached this part of the tube, another yellow has been discharged. When the movements of the egg tube again become normal, the complete egg and the recently liberated yolk are carried downward very close together. The glands in the wall of the tube apply white, membranes and shell around both the yellow and the complete egg. The resulting oversize egg is then deposited as a double egg, probably to the pride, and certainly to the relief, of the responsible hen.

Do Roosters Ever Lay Eggs?

Very small eggs, sometimes only one-tenth the normal size, are occasionally found in hen's nests. Some people believe that these small eggs are laid by old roosters or cocks, and they are therefore sometimes called "cock" eggs. However, no rooster is capable of laying an egg of any size. The small eggs are laid by hens and are thought to be the result of a disturbance of the egg-producing mechanism. In some instances, a yolk smaller than normal is discharged from the ovary; in other cases, a loosened piece of tissue or other substance gains access to the oviduct, passes downward and in the regular way is coated with white, membranes and shell. Usually the disturbance is temporary and the hen shortly produces normal eggs again.

What Bird Lays the Largest Eggs?

The egg of the ostrich is larger than that of any other living bird. Some investigators have amused themselves by breaking hens' eggs into the empty shell of an ostrich egg and, from these experiments, have found that an ostrich egg shell will hold from twelve to eighteen hens' eggs.

Ostrich eggs measure six to seven inches in length and five to six inches in diameter and, incidentally, require about forty minutes or longer for thorough boiling.

Although the ostrich egg seems huge when compared with the eggs of most living birds, there are some extinct species that would have probably been chagrined if they had laid an egg so small. The extinct elephant bird, or roc, of Madagascar, produced the largest egg that anyone knows anything about. As I have mentioned elsewhere, almost complete shells of these eggs have been discovered, some of them measuring thirteen inches in length and nine and a half inches in diameter. The shell will hold more than two gallons, which is six times as much as an ostrich egg will hold, and nearly 150 times the capacity of a hen's egg.

Hummingbirds produce the smallest eggs. Some of the smallest species, the vervair hummingbirds of Haiti and Jamaica, lay eggs that are only a quarter of an inch in length.

How Many Eggs Can a Duck or Chicken Lay in One Year?

Poultry breeders are continuously trying to improve the egg-laying ability of their fowls. So far as I know, the ideal of one egg a day for 365 days has not quite been achieved, but the present record is not far short of the mark. Champion ducks frequently outlay chickens. In 1927, the world's duck record for egg laying was 363 eggs for 365 days, while the champion hen produced only 351 eggs for the same period. As of 1946, the world's record for chickens was held by an Australorp hen of Australia, which laid 361 eggs in 365 days, a considerable increase over the record for 1927, but still somewhat short of the champion duck record. I have not found any records for ducks later than the one mentioned above.

Egg-laying contests in the United States are conducted on a basis of points, in which the quality of the egg is considered in addition to the total number produced. The present record for this country (1946) is held by a Rhode Island red hen which produced 351 eggs in 357 days for a total score of 386.10 points.

What Birds Do Not Incubate Their Eggs?

Although most birds incubate their eggs by sitting on them, a few species have found ways to relieve themselves of the chore. One of the most ingenious methods has been perfected by the mound birds or megapodes of Australia, the East Indies and adjacent areas. These birds scratch together a large pile of sticks, leaves and dirt, lay their eggs near the top of the mound, and then cover them. The heat from the sun and the heat generated as the vegetation decomposes hatches the eggs. Several birds use the same place year after year, building a community incubator, so that some of the mounds are fourteen or fifteen feet high and thirty to thirty-five feet in diameter. The crocodile bird of Africa makes use of a similar principle; it lays its eggs in the sand where they are hatched solely by the heat of the sun.

Husbands That Do the Household Chores

The males of several kinds of birds help in the incubation of the eggs, but the outstanding example of a henpecked husband is the phalarope, several species of which are found in the United States. Phalaropes are medium-sized birds with long beaks and long legs and have the same general appearance as sandpipers, except that the female is more brilliantly colored than the male, a condition that seldom occurs among birds. The male builds the nest, is courted by the female and, after the eggs are laid, takes over the entire responsibility of incubating them.

The assistance given by any male bird during incubation is not entirely unselfish. During the incubation season, some birds develop areas of inflammation on their breasts, called hatching spots, which are somewhat irritating, and it is believed that the coolness of the egg surface relieves the irritation. In any case, in those species in which only the female develops the spots, the male does not help in the incubation process where the inflamed area develops in both sexes of the species, the male invariably takes his turn on the nest.

Can Any Bird Fly When Hatched?

Many kinds of birds when first hatched have practically no feathers, and it is several days or even weeks before they are able to fly. An outstanding exception is the brush turkey or mound builder of Australia and adjacent areas. The young birds when hatched have a complete coat of feathers and are able to fly almost immediately.

Do Any Birds Hibernate?

Before it was known that many birds migrated, various weird theories were advanced to explain their disappearance from certain regions during a part of the year. One idea was that birds hibernated during the winter in caves, hollow trees and similar places. Swallows, for instance, were said to hibernate in the mud at the bottom of lakes and streams. In fact, a recently compiled list of books and articles dealing with the hiberation of swallows contained no less than 175 titles. Despite these early beliefs and the learned published articles, however, so far as is known there are no types of birds that hibernate. During the winter, they simply migrate to warmer regions.

Even after some of the facts of migration were known, a number of strange theories prevailed. One of the most interesting was that the larger birds, especially cranes, carried the smaller birds on their backs during the migratory flight. It is now known that this does not happen, but the belief is still prevalent in some places. During the past fifty years a considerable amount of work has been done on bird migration, but it still presents many unsolved problems. Many factors are known to influence migration —amount of food available, relative length of day and night, temperature and changes in the birds' reproductive organs at different periods of the year—but a number of other factors not yet discovered probably also play a part.

What Bird Travels 20,000 Miles a Year?

Several species of birds have long migratory routes, but the champion migrants of them all are the arctic terns. These amazing birds make a round-trip migration each year of 20,000 to 22,000 miles, although probably not all of them fly quite that far. They nest over a wide range, from the arctic circle as far south as Massachusetts; in winter some are found even within the antarctic circle. It is thought that the tern makes the trip in about twenty weeks, averaging over 1000 miles a week. This seems even more remarkable when one remembers that much of the time is spent searching for food. The arctic tern experiences more daylight than any other animal. Traveling back and forth between the arctic and the antarctic, and in its nesting and winter quarters, it is constantly in areas where the daylight hours are longest.

Most land birds make comparatively short hops during their migrations, but some must fly for long distances over open water with no chance to alight on land. The golden plovers make the longest nonstop flight over open ocean. The American golden plover, which nests in the arctic region of North America, starts its southern flight from Labrador or Nova Scotia and, so far as is known, flies directly to northern South America, a distance of 2400 to 2500 miles. This is thought to be a nonstop flight, but some biologists suspect that the birds may rest occasionally on the water. The Pacific golden plover also takes a remarkable migratory route over open ocean. After its nesting season is over in Alaska, Siberia and adjacent regions, it migrates to Hawaii.

Do Birds Migrate on the Same Day Each Year?

No birds begin their migration on the same day each year, but there are some that do not vary the day a great deal. Probably the most remarkable in this respect is the slender-billed shearwater or mutton bird, a marine bird that nests in countless thousands on Phillips and Green Islands between Tasmania and southern Australia. Year in and year out there may be a few days' difference in the time of their arrival, but once a few stragglers start flying in the time of arrival of the rest, according to Ludlow Griscom, well-known ornithologist, can be predicted almost to the quarter hour. If a few birds arrive on, say, Monday, November 22, the mass of the breeding population is almost sure to arrive at Green Island on Wednesday, November 24 at 8 P. M.

The cliff swallows of Capistrano, California, also have a famous reputation for regularity; they furnish material for sensational newspaper articles once or twice each year. Cliff swallows nest in colonies and build their flask-shaped mud nests in a variety of places including banks, the eaves of buildings and other sheltered spots. Some of these birds have nested for years at the San Juan Capistrano Mission, and an interesting tale has grown up regarding the regularity with which this colony enters upon its migration. According to the story, the swallows always leave the mission on October 23 for their southward migration and, as regular as clockwork, return on March 19. Nor does the extra day in leap years confuse them; if we are to believe reports, they take this change into consideration, since they still depart and arrive on their favorite dates! Observations of biologists have failed to confirm the reported regularity of their migration; the dates of departure and arrival have been found to vary from year to year. Despite scientific opinion, however, newspapers will continue to have a biennial field day with the legend.

What Is the Largest Bird in the World?

The largest living bird, as far as height and weight are concerned, is the African ostrich. It does not even have any close competition for this honor. Large males have been found to measure eight feet in height, and the maximum size is probably over eight feet, with a weight of more than 300 pounds.

Some extinct birds were considerably larger than ostriches, notably the moas, a group of ostrichlike birds whose remains have been found in New Zealand. Almost complete skeletons nine to ten feet in height have been discovered, and it is thought that the largest of them were almost twelve feet high. However, there is no evidence that they ever attained a height of eighteen feet, as some textbooks have stated. Another extinct group of birds, the elephant birds of Madagascar, were more massively built than the moas and produced larger eggs, but they were probably not so tall.

What Birds Have the Greatest Wing Spread?

The two groups of birds that have the largest spread are the albatrosses and the condors, but there is no evidence that either of them has a wing spread of seventeen or eighteen feet, as has been reported. A recent edition of a well-known encyclopedia, for instance, states that the albatross may have a wing spread of seventeen feet, but an expert on birds of this type, Robert Cushman Murphy of the American Museum, says that this figure is far too high. The maximum spread for the wandering albatross is probably eleven feet four inches, a figure that represents the wing spread of the largest of hundreds of specimens measured by several different men. As for the condor, although greater spreads have been reported, the largest recent measurement that I have found was a fraction over ten feet, for a condor shot by Murphy off the coast of Peru.

Birds

The bird weighed twenty-eight and a half pounds. Some biologists still maintain that the condor has the greater wing spread, but others, including myself, favor the albatross.

The wing spreads of a few species of large birds are indicated in the table below.

CHART OF WING SPREADS

Species	Probable Maximum Wing Spread	Remarks
Wandering albatross	11 to 12 feet	11 feet 4 inches is the largest spread by actual measurement that can be accepted at present.
Condors	10 to 11 feet	The largest recent measurement of a South American condor which I have found was slightly over 10 feet.
King vulture	9 to 10 feet	Found in northern South America, Mexico and Central America.
White pelican	8 to 9 feet	Found in Canada and south to Yellowstone Park. In winter occurs along the Gulf Coast of the United States.
Great bustard	8 to 9 feet	A large gooselike game bird related to the cranes. Rather widely distributed in parts of Europe, Asia and Africa.
Bald eagle	7 to 8 feet	Widely distributed over Canada, the United States and on south into Mexico.

Animal Facts *and* Fallacies

Species	Probable Maximum Wing Spread	Remarks
Golden eagle	7 to 8 feet	Widely distributed in North America, Europe and Asia. In the United States, more common west of the Mississippi River.
Man-o-war or frigate bird	7 to 8 feet	Found in the United States chiefly off the coast of Florida. Also occurs farther south.
Whooping crane	7 to 8 feet	Found chiefly in Canada, although it migrates as far south as Texas in winter. Now exceedingly rare.
Sandhill crane	6 to 7 feet	Rather widely distributed in Canada and the United States, but quite shy and seldom seen by the average person.
Brown pelican	6 to 7 feet	Occurs along the Atlantic and Gulf coasts of the United States and south into Central and South America.
Turkey vulture or buzzard	6 to 7 feet	I once measured a specimen with a wing spread of exactly 6 feet. Found over most of the United States and south into Central and South America.

How Fast Can Birds Fly?

Before the development of automobiles, airplanes, stop watches and other devices that could help accurately determine the swiftness of bird flight, various wild estimates had been made. Even some biologists thought that migration flights were made at incredible speeds of as much as 400 to 500 miles an hour.

Within recent years a large number of accurate records have been procured. The airplane, particularly, has made it possible to obtain records over longer distances. Observations from automobiles, while useful, are more limited, since the bird is quite likely to fly off the course or road with a total disregard for the stranded fuming observer.

Although the flight speed of many birds has been considerably exaggerated, some species can fly at astonishingly fast rates. The fastest flight speed on record was established by two species of swifts in India which were timed over a measured course of two miles. It was found that these birds covered the distance in from thirty-six to forty-two seconds, or at the rate of 171.4 to 200 miles an hour. Some swifts in Mesopotamia overtook and circled an airplane which was flying at sixty-eight miles an hour, which means that they were probably flying at a speed of nearly 100 miles an hour.

Aside from the swifts, the fastest birds are probably the duck hawks and their relatives. A European peregrine, a species frequently used in falconry, was timed with a stop watch during its dive after quarry, and was estimated to have been flying at 165 to 180 miles an hour. The duck hawk in the United States, since it easily overtakes and attacks such swift birds as ducks and pigeons, probably flies at approximately 100 miles an hour. Other birds of prey have also been reported as flying at 100 to 120 miles an hour.

Ostriches, emus and similar birds cannot fly, but their running speed somewhat compensates for this handicap. Of this group the ostrich is the fastest; from all available evidence, it is the fastest running bird in the world. One ostrich was timed at the rate of fifty miles an hour, a speed it could maintain for at least a half mile.

The possible flying speed of some of the fastest birds, aside from those already mentioned, is indicated in the table below. Many of these figures have been checked by several investigators, so that most of them should represent a fair degree of accuracy.

CHART OF FLIGHT SPEEDS

Species	Possible Speed in Miles per Hour	Remarks
Golden plover	60 to 65	A record of 60 miles an hour was obtained when these birds were chased by an airplane; speeds up to 70 miles an hour have also been reported.
Mourning dove	60 to 65	At least one bird has been timed at 60 miles an hour.
Carrier or homing pigeons	60 to 65	An occasional pigeon has averaged 60 miles an hour over known courses of a few

Birds

Species	Possible Speed in Miles per Hour	Remarks
		miles, and as much as 55 miles an hour for 4 hours.
Ducks and geese	55 to 60	Varies considerably with the species, the usual speeds listed being from 42 to 59 miles an hour. One canvas back duck was reported to have reached 72 miles an hour when pursued by airplane, but this speed seems somewhat excessive in view of other records.
Starlings	45 to 50	
Hummingbirds	50 to 55	
Wading birds (sandpipers, curlews, etc.)	45 to 50	
Gannet	45 to 50	A large, white, gooselike ocean bird, with black wing feathers.
Stork	45 to 50	There are no true storks in the United States, although a related species, the wood ibis, is found along the Gulf coast and sometimes farther north.
Swallows	45 to 50	Usual flight speed from 24 to 31 miles an hour.
Crows	40 to 45	Usual flight speed 20 to 30 miles an hour.

What Birds' Nests Are Used For Soup?

In parts of Asia and many islands of the Pacific, there is a species of swift, similar to the chimney swift or chimney "sweep" of the United States and other countries, which nests in caves in large numbers. The nests are made primarily of a secretion from the birds' mouths, which hardens into a gelatinous mass. After the young birds have finished polluting the nests and have flown away, the nests are collected for people with indiscriminate appetites, supposedly being thoroughly cleaned of any stray feathers or other "foreign" material before they are served. These nests, which are used principally for making birds' nest soup, may sell for as much as $25.00 a pound.

A Bird That Hatches Its Eggs in Prison

The nesting habits of some of the hornbills are about as remarkable as any to be found among birds. When a pair of hornbills have the urge to build a nest, they find a hollow tree with an opening large enough to admit the female. She builds a nest inside the hollow, while the male gathers mud and debris and cements up the entrance, leaving only a small opening through which he can feed his mate. One to several eggs are laid, depending upon the species of hornbill, and while the female is incubating the eggs and rearing the young the male brings her food regularly. He literally runs himself ragged: by the time the female and the young emerge from the hollow, the male is a skinny and bedraggled-looking specimen. If he should be killed during the nesting period, the female and her young probably would not starve in their prison, for it has been reported that other male hornbills in the vicinity come to the rescue and take over the duties of the unfortunate spouse.

This strange nesting habit is of considerable importance in the life of the hornbill family, not only because the eggs or young are thus protected from hungry enemies, but because during the nesting period the female is incapable of flight. While she is incubating the eggs and rearing the young, she sheds her feathers and grows a new coat. When she at last emerges from her prison, she is resplendent in brand new clothes, an extreme contrast indeed to the poor male who does not regain his former neat appearance for many days.

Hornbills are large birds found in India, the Malay Peninsula and adjacent regions. They have big bills or beaks, and in some species a large crest rises from the base of the bill. Noticeable eyelashes are present, a feature not common among birds. The bills, despite their size, are not so heavy as they appear, since they are at least partially hollow and therefore relatively light in weight. One species, however, has a large, solid bill, which is so hard that it has been used for carvings in place of ivory. In some regions the bills of these birds are so much in demand for love charms that the bird is exceedingly rare.

Do Any Birds Milk Goats?

In parts of Europe the belief that some birds milk goats used to be so firmly ingrained that the name of goatsuckers was given to the suspected birds. Even today, this common name is applied to the group of birds which includes the nighthawks, the chuck-will's-widows and the whippoorwills.

Although they do not milk goats, the goatsucker group has other habits that are almost as interesting. Most of the birds feed chiefly upon insects which they capture in flight. They have enormous mouths set with bristles, which make very efficient fly traps, and have been known to swallow even smaller birds with a single gulp. They also all have the unusual habit of perching lengthwise, rather than crosswise, on limbs.

Nighthawks, which may be found in large numbers in a limited area, are seen more often than the other species in this group. During the summer and fall these birds may fly at any hour of the day, but late afternoon is a favorite time. They can fly swiftly, but sometimes they are obviously not in a hurry. During the breeding season, especially, a male nighthawk may frequently be seen fluttering along, gradually climbing higher and higher, its harsh cry intermittently breaking the silence. Suddenly it will partially fold its pointed wings and dive headfirst so swiftly that one wonders how it can keep from being dashed to death. Near the ground, however, it straightens its wings and zooms upward, the vibration of its wing feathers making a dull booming sound. Apparently some people think that the sound resembles the bellow of a bull, because the name of bullbat for this bird is much more common in some areas than is nighthawk.

What Wild Birds Are Responsible For an Industry?

The Chincha Islands lie off the western coast of Peru. On these small dots of land live the most valuable birds in the world. For centuries, great numbers of sea birds have been nesting on these islands, and their droppings accumulated until the material was many feet thick in some places. At last someone got the bright idea that this guano would make excellent fertilizer, and it was consequently removed and sent all over the world by the shipload. For many years guano from the Chincha Islands supplied much of the world's fertilizer, to the great satisfaction of the Peruvian Government and everyone connected with the industry. Within recent years other types of fertilizer have tended to replace guano, but it is still used to some extent.

The majority of the birds that nest on the islands are a kind of cormorant, appropriately called guanjays, or guanays, but other sea birds such as gulls, terns and pelicans are well represented. In some parts of the islands the birds produce guano at the rate of 750 tons an acre per year, which gives one an idea of the tremendous numbers of birds involved.

Visitors who have seen these islands say that the nesting birds are not especially afraid of human beings, and that in some places the nests on the ground are so numerous that one has difficulty walking through the pecking, squawking females. But man-made vehicles such as airplanes and steamships do bother them, and now rigid laws prevent the approach of airplanes and the blowing of ships' sirens in the vicinity of the islands, lest the disturbance cause the birds to seek more isolated areas for their nests.

Birds That Catch Fish For Men

Cormorants are large birds with webbed feet and hooked beaks that feed almost entirely on fish. They capture their food by diving into the water and using both legs and wings to overhaul their prey. They frequently seem to fish for sheer enjoyment, for they sometimes continue fishing after they have stuffed themselves to capacity.

In parts of the Orient, natives have taken practical advantage of the cormorant's ability as a fisherman. Young birds are caught and trained to fish for the natives rather than for themselves. At first, each bird has a ring around its neck to prevent it from swallowing the fish it catches, but eventually some of them become so well trained that they can be trusted without ring or leash and will not swallow a fish until given permission to do so. The birds are trained to bring their catch to the boats, where they are frequently rewarded with bits of fish or with fish too small to be of commercial value.

Sometimes several cormorants may co-operate and round up scattered fish into compact and more easily caught shoals, and two or more may gang up on a fish too large for a single bird to manage. Well-trained birds are of considerable value to their owners; it has been said that some cormorants may catch as many as one hundred fish in an hour.

What Bird Carries Its Young in Its Beak?

Hooded mergansers, a species of duck, usually build their nests in hollow trees, frequently some distance from the water. Most young ducks start swimming soon after hatching, and for a long time no one knew how the young mergansers got to the water before they could fly. It is now known that they are helped by the female bird and, although they sometimes receive rather rough treatment in the process, apparently they are seldom injured. Sometimes the mother bird simply tumbles them unceremoniously from the nest and then leads them to the water. Sometimes however, she performs one of the most amazing acts in the bird world: she takes a duckling in her beak, flies with it to the water and then returns for the others.

The hooded merganser has been given various common names, including fish duck, tree duck and sheldrake. The male is easy to identify by the crest of long feathers on the back and top of its head. The head and neck are black except for a large white spot on the fan-shaped crest. The female is not so easy to distinguish from related birds.

Woodcocks, birds with long beaks, related to sandpipers, also have a novel way of moving their young from place to place. If disturbed, a female woodcock will frequently pick up one of her young between her feet and legs, and fly off with it. If she has the opportunity, she will move all the young birds to a place of safety in this way.

How Does the Pelican Use Its Pouch?

The long beak of the pelican, with the large pouch attached to its lower jaw, makes it one of the most peculiar looking of all birds. However, not only is the large pouch of considerable use to the adult pelican, but without it the young pelicans would not get fed nearly so well.

Pelicans feed primarily on fish, and the pouch is a very efficient fish net. If the bird, as it flies along, sights a fish in the water below, it drops like a rock with a splash that can be heard for half a mile. If there is only a single fish the pelican will seize and swallow it, but if there is a shoal, the pelican is really in its element. It swims forward, using its pouch as a scoop net. When the pouch is full of water and fish, the bird closes its mouth, and the water drains out leaving the fish safely caught in the pouch. If the fishing is good, the pelican may not stop to eat, but may rush back into the game until its bag is bulging. The capacity of the pouch is enormous, and it can be stretched

considerably; one writer states that it can hold as much as 40 pounds of fish. However, I doubt if even such a large bird as a pelican could keep from falling on its face with so heavy a load; certainly it could not fly.

The pouch, like all good fish nets, is dried or at least aired occasionally. The bird tilts its head backward and opens its beak widely, causing the pouch to spread out over its chest. There the pelican stands, with its mouth agape and its bare pouch hanging out, certainly one of the most ridiculous sights in the bird world.

Young pelicans are fed by regurgitation, and the pouch makes a handy serving bowl. The mother pelican opens her mouth, burps, and a quart or so of ill-smelling but wholly enjoyable fish soup flows into the pouch. The young stick their heads in and greedily consume the contents of the pouch, sometimes almost falling into it in their eagerness to get their stomachs full. It was at one time thought that live fish in water were carried in the pouch to the young, but there is no evidence to support this theory.

How Long Do Birds Live?

Parrots, various kinds of eaglelike birds and swans are credited with sometimes living for 100 to 300 years. Even in relatively recent publications one finds reports of a vulture that lived to be 118 years old; a parrot, 120; and a golden eagle, 104. Most of these reports are for birds that were alive several hundred years ago; not even seventy-five years has been claimed for a bird in a relatively modern zoological park. Men who have investigated bird ages admit that some may live longer than presently established ages indicate, but until such extreme ages are verified these reported centenarians must be looked upon with suspicion.

Established bird ages include an eagle-owl of sixty-eight, a condor of fifty-two, a parrot of fifty-four, an eagle of fifty-five and a white pelican of fifty-one. Even some of the smaller birds live for a surprisingly long time. Accepted ages for small birds include a starling of seventeen, a canary of twenty-two, an English sparrow of twenty-three and a red-crested cardinal of thirty. The late Major **Stanley** Flower, who has probably done more work investigating animal ages than any other man, believed that birds in general live longer than do mammals.

PART THREE
Fish

What Are Fish?

Anyone who looks in *Webster* will find that a fish is a "cold-blooded, strictly aquatic, water-breathing vertebrate having the limbs (when present) developed as fins, and typically a long, scaly, somewhat tapering body ending in a broad vertical caudal fin." Although most fish do possess scales of one type or another, there are nevertheless a few like the catfish and the ocean sunfish which are entirely scaleless. The limbs of fish, in the form of fins attached along the side or lower part of the body, are so formed in some groups that the front pair allow the fish to crawl along the bottom of pond or ocean; or even in a few cases, to scramble about on land. Breathing is accomplished by gills which are placed just back of the head and usually covered by gill covers. However, many species have an organ called the air or swim bladder which, in some fish, is connected to the region just behind the mouth. For these forms, the swim bladder functions as a lung, and the fish can come to the surface of the water and take in air.

It should be noted that whales, porpoises, dolphins, manitees and similar animals are mammals, not fish, although they share the water habitat with fish and in general appearance are quite similar to fish.

What Happens to Deep Sea Fish
Brought Suddenly to the Surface?

The organ called a swim or air bladder helps some deep sea fish to adjust their bodies to different water depths. At great depths, the air bladder contains a tremendous amount of air, but the water pressure prevents it from expanding. Normally fish move slowly from deep to shallow water and the excess air is absorbed, permitting the fish to be comfortable at different depths. But if a fish in deep water is suddenly brought to the surface, things happen which are most uncomfortable for it. When the pressure of the water that has been holding the gas within bounds is suddenly released, allowing the gas to expand, the stomach of the fish is pushed out of its mouth. A fish in this condition will usually die if it is tossed back into the water, but if some compassionate person should stick a pin through its side, the extra gas would escape, the stomach would return to its proper position and the fish might swim off none the worse for its harrowing experience.

Can Fish Change Color?

Some years ago I was idly watching some fish swimming about in a clear park stream, the bottom of which was peculiarly marked with large areas of contrasting light and dark spots. As the fish swam about searching for food, they would occasionally stop for a short time over one of these areas and within a few minutes, much to my amazement, they would become almost invisible. I watched for an hour or more, and they always changed color to harmonize with the background. Many species of fish have this power of color change developed to a certain extent, but some are much more adept than others. Some of the flatfish, including the flounders and the turbots, are probably the champion blenders of the fish world. Experiments have shown that if they are placed even on a checkboard background, within a short time it is almost impossible to tell where background ends and fish begins.

The Stickleback, Champion Nest Builder

Many fish build nests of one type or another, but the small sticklebacks—most species are only a few inches in length—are probably the champions of them all. The nests are built by the male from twigs, stems, leaves and similar rubbish, which, using his mouth, he fashions into a hollow structure with a single entrance, cementing the material with a sticky substance secreted by glands connected to the kidneys.

The nest when commpleted is a comparatively elaborate structure usually attached to reeds or some other suitable foundation. The stickleback then sallies forth in search of a wife whom, by persuasion, or even by such strong-arm methods as sticking her with his spines, he induces to enter the nest. Once inside, the female deposits the eggs and then breaks through the back wall of the nest and swims away. The males of some species are not satisfied with a single conquest but, after fertilizing the eggs, go out and repeat the whole process. When sufficient eggs have been procured from females willing to be pilfered, the male guards the nest until the eggs are hatched and the young are old enough to shift for themselves.

Fish That Blow Bubbles

Several kinds of fish, including the Siamese fighting fish, the paradise fish and the gouramis, make nests by blowing bubbles from their mouths. Several of these bubble nesters have recently become popular as aquarium fish, and their nesting habits are well known to many fish fanciers. The nest is built by the male bubble fish who goes to the surface of the water, takes some air into his mouth and blows a number of bubbles which stick together and float on top of the water. He then goes on the prowl for a wife, whom he herds under the bubble nest. After the eggs have been deposited and fertilized, the male takes the eggs in his mouth, encases them in a bubble and releases them so that they will float upward and stick to the nest.

The male then chases the female away and himself guards the nest and repairs it until the eggs are hatched. In many cases the male will swim with his brood for a time, fighting any enemy that appears, but he frequently loses all his parental feeling after a few days of careful watchfulness and may suddenly dash forward and devour all that he can catch. The young scatter in all directions, and fortunately a few avoid their greedy parent and escape to carry on the race.

A Mouth Full of Eggs

The males of some marine catfish and others found in the rivers of South America, carry the eggs in their mouths until they hatch. So far as known, they do not eat at all during this period. The father's interest in his duties does not wane even after the young fish hatch. He swims with them for a time and, when danger threatens, holds his mouth open until the frightened youngsters can dash in to safety.

In all fairness to the female sex, it should be mentioned that in the case of some African fish related to the perch, the female rather than the male carries the eggs in her mouth and, in time of danger, allows the young fish to seek safety therein.

A Male Fish That Grows on the Body of the Female

While the female angler fish may measure three feet or more and weigh twenty or thirty pounds, the tiny males of some species have a maximum length of about four inches, and in some cases are so small that they can be seen only with difficulty.

A short time after hatching, the male attaches himself to the body of the female, and although the female continues to grow the male does not, to any extent. The tissues of the two fuse together, and the two blood systems become connected. After this happens, the male is absolutely dependent upon the female, and draws nourishment from her blood stream. In 1936, one of these female anglers was caught in a net off the coast of Massachusetts at a depth of 600 feet. This fish was thirty-three and a half inches long and it weighed twenty pounds. Study revealed that a tiny male, only one and a half inches in length was attached to the skin of the female's body just behind the gill covers.

It is not known why this peculiar association should have developed, but its advantages are apparent. Most anglers of this type are deep sea fish and live in relative darkness most of their lives. Since the two sexes are attached almost from birth, when the breeding season arrives the males and females do not have to go blundering around in the darkness seeking a mate. Comparable associations between male and female animals without backbones are known, but the angler fish are the only known vertebrates in which such a situation occurs.

Hobo Fish

Shark suckers (other names include sucking fish, pilot fish and remora) are slender grayish fish two to three feet long. On top of their heads is an oblong suckerlike disc, with which they attach themselves to almost any kind of moving object such as whales, turtles, or even ships, although they are most often found associated with sharks. The reason for their peculiar habit is not entirely clear. They do gain a certain amount of protection from their hosts and sometimes eat scraps of food left by them. They also gain free transportation, but the shark sucker is a good swimmer and indeed can frequently swim faster than the shark to which it is attached. Possibly they are just naturally lazy and prefer to spend their energies in ways other than swimming.

Contrary to popular opinion, the shark sucker does not directly harm the shark by attaching to it. However, if a shark is host to several suckers, it must expend considerably more muscular effort in swimming. Very thin sharks have been found to which several of the sucking fish were attached, and it is thought probable that these hobos contributed to the shark's poor physical condition.

In some parts of the world, especially in the South Seas, natives use the shark suckers as fish hooks. They tie a line to the tail of a sucking fish and, when the game, fish or turtle, is spotted, toss the remora overboard. It is allowed to swim about until it fastens onto its prey, which is then slowly hauled within capturing or harpooning distance. A remora attaches to its host so firmly that it is almost impossible to pull it off without tearing its sucker.

At one time it was believed that shark suckers could stop ships. According to one story, it was a large shark sucker that attached itself to Marc Antony's ship, thus delaying his arrival for the battle of Actium and thereby causing his defeat.

Fish That Trick Their Prey

There are fish, called angler fish, that have very peculiar, suggestive devices for attracting their prey—usually lures of some kind which float above their mouths. In certain cases the lures are simply movable barbules, while in others the resemblance of the lure to a fishing rod and line is remarkable. In some species there is even a three-pronged hook on the end of the line. Many names have been given to the more common species, including fishing frog, goose fish, toadfish and allmouth. This last name is especially appropriate since, when its mouth is open, the fish looks like a large mouth with a small body attached to it. The angler's habit is to lie buried in the mud or otherwise concealed, with its lure dangling over its wide open mouth. Any fish that has the curiosity to investigate the dangling lure disappears with a dull snap down the cavernous maw.

Angler fish will eat practically any living thing that comes within reach, even an occasional sea bird. A rather remarkable story has been told about two boys, an angler fish, and a duck, on the eastern coast of the United States. The two boys were fishing close to shore when they were attracted by the peculiar actions of a flock of ducks some distance away. Some of the ducks appeared to be diving tail first, and all the birds seemed to be somewhat alarmed. The boys rowed toward the ducks and, as they approached, saw a huge angler fish in the clear water come close to the surface, seize a duck and swallow it. The boys went back to shore for a harpoon and returned to the place where they had seen the fish. When they spotted the angler on the shallow bottom, they harpooned it, towed it to shore, and then were surprised to see that its sides were moving rather vigorously. Concluding that it must be the duck, they cut open the fish and found the duck, still alive, but covered with the angler's stomach secretions. When cleaned, the duck was none the worse for its experience and the boys kept it as a pet for some time, naming it, quite appropriately, Davy Jones.

Fish That Swallow Bigger Fish

Imagine if you can a man weighing 150 pounds sitting down to a table and eating a 300-pound hog at one meal and, what is more, swallowing it whole. Angler fish regularly and successfully (thanks to the stretching powers of their stomachs) swallow objects that are larger than their own bodies. Their voracious appetite, however, sometimes makes them overly ambitious. Specimens have been found floating helplessly at the water's surface with fish in their stomachs which were more than twice their own size. However, appetite alone is not to blame. Their teeth are so arranged that once they have seized a victim they cannot turn it loose. The angler must finish any meal it begins or endure being dragged through the water by its prey.

Some species of deep sea fish, smaller than the anglers, equal or even exceed the angler in swallowing ability. These fish, which include the black or great swallower and the so-called widemouths, customarily swallow fish larger than they are and are reported to have successfully downed fish three times their own size.

Fish That Swell Like Balloons

One of the oddest types of defense found in fish is that used by the puffer, globe and porcupine fish. They are able to inflate their bodies to several times normal size by taking air or water into a special bladderlike sac connected with the gullet or esophagus. When one of their enemies, such as an enterprising shark, swims into view, these fish immediately start swelling, presumably discouraging the astonished pursuer. Some species have inedible spines scattered over their bodies, so that when they are inflated they look more like pincushions than tasty morsels. Many of the fish that employ this type of defense are forced to float on top of the water like balloons until the air is expelled.

Their ability to inflate themselves is curious enough, but an even more remarkable habit was reported many years ago by Charles Darwin. According to his story, it would be disastrous for any shark to eat one of these fish, because the fish would gnaw through the stomach and body wall of the shark to get out. Darwin reported this story in good faith, and until recently it was believed by many biologists. Now, however, it is regarded simply as a fish story, too good to be true.

Flying Fish

One of the most interesting experiences of an ocean voyage is to see a school of flying fish suddenly break the surface and go sailing over the waves like so many streaks of light. The "wings" of flying fish are variants of the normal front fins, in that they are greatly enlarged. In flight, these fins are spread and held at an angle to the body; some species also spread the rear pair of fins. It was at one time thought that the fish flapped its fins like the wings of a bird, but this is not true. The fish swims rapidly through the water, with part of its body breaking the surface. It may swim in this fashion for some distance, gaining speed by vigorous movements of the tail. When the fins are spread and held rigid, its speed lifts it bodily into the air, and it may sail or glide for several hundred yards before dropping back into the ocean. It can lengthen the initial flight by striking the crests of the waves and picking up additional power with a few vigorous strokes of its tail. It may fly quite high—not infrequently flying fish land by accident upon the decks of large steamers.

Fish That Climb Trees

Travelers in India, the Far East and parts of Africa are likely to be astonished at the sight of small fish skipping nimbly about on land. Perhaps the most efficient of these land scramblers are the climbing perch and the mud skippers. The common eel also has been known to make excursions overland, but it is not so efficient as the fish mentioned above.

The climbing perch of India and adjacent areas are small fish that vary in length from about three to eight inches. They get about by spreading the rows of movable spines on their gill covers so as to brace themselves on the ground, and pushing vigorously with tail and front fins. The gills of these land-inhabiting forms have become modified so that they can breathe in the air for a time.

The first definite report of the climbing prowess of these fish was made in 1797 by someone who caught a climbing perch on the trunk of a tree five feet above ground and apparently trying to climb higher. Since that time, specimens have been found in rather high branches of trees, and although some biologists believe that these fish were dropped by birds others think that they definitely can climb, especially if the tree trunk is growing at an angle. At any rate, the fish are called climbing perch, and the name is likely to stick.

The mud skippers of Africa, Asia and Australia are even more efficient than the climbing perch. They can climb up leaning trees and up on logs in search of insects; in some places they are called tree climbing gobies. In appearance, the mud skippers have features of both tadpoles and frogs. The front part of the body is enlarged and tapers toward the tail like the body of a tadpole, while the head is surmounted by a pair of toadlike bulging eyes. With their modified front fins, the creatures are able to skip about on land rather rapidly. When not actively searching for food, the mud skipper frequently rests on the edge of the bank with its tail in the water. The tail region is so richly supplied with blood vessels that the fish gets some oxygen from the water through this part of the body to supplement the air breathing it can do through its modified gills.

What Fish Can Live Out of Water?

Droughts hold no terrors for the lungfish of Africa. When the swamps and streams start drying up, these fish simply burrow into the mud for a foot or so, fashion themselves comfortable rooms and coil up for a nice summer's sleep. They secrete a mucus that, mixed with the mud, hardens and forms a kind of cocoon about their bodies. Air is obtained through a small opening that is left at the top of the burrow, and most breathing is carried on during this period by the swim bladder, which is really a well-developed lung.

Under ordinary conditions, the fish remain in their sleeping quarters until the rains come again and flood their sun-baked homes. Thanks to their habit of forming cocoons, lungfish are to be seen in many aquariums throughout the world. Collectors locate the buried fish by pounding on the earth until they find a spot that sounds hollow. The fish are then dug up, packed and shipped, cocoon and all. At their new quarters, the cocoons are placed in water and when the mud has dissolved the lungfish swim happily about.

Fish

A Fish Said to Raid Hen Houses

A. Hyatt Verrill, well-known writer and South American explorer, relates one of the most amazing fish stories that this writer has ever heard. His story concerns the South American lungfish, which is a peculiar and somewhat large fish found in the rivers and swamps of northeastern and central South America. In certain areas when the rivers and swamps dry up, as they do occasionally, the fish reportedly get out on land in search of food which, during this period, consists of lizards, mice, rats and similar creatures. According to Verrill, the lungfish is not satisfied with catching wild animals, but frequently turns marauder and raids the hen houses of natives living near the stream! It is well known that some fish, such as the angler, will eat ducks or other birds if they happen to get within reach, but that a fish should go hunting for chickens across dry land is really incredible. However, in parts of South America, according to the story, these raids are accepted without furor by the owners of the chickens, who simply capture the thief and have fish for their next meal instead of chicken.

What Fish Has Four Eyes?

In parts of Central and South America there are fish that have eyes unlike those of any other vertebrate animal. They are called four-eyed fish but, although the structure of their eyes is remarkable, the term "four-eyed" is somewhat misleading. There are only two eye sockets and in each eye socket there is only a single eye, but the eyes are constructed for two types of vision. The fish are sometimes called double-eyed fish, a name more descriptive of the actual construction of the eyes. Each eye is divided into an upper and lower part by a dark stripe, and the fish usually swims with its head partly out of the water so that the water surface lies along the dividing line of the eye. Detailed studies of the structure of the eyes indicate that these fish have double vision. The upper half of the eye is thus probably used for seeing objects out of the water, while the lower half peers around for food beneath the surface.

Fish Whose Eyes Migrate

A flounder, when laid on its side, will stare up with both eyes at the same time. In most fish the eyes are on opposite sides of the head, and only one is visible when the fish is laid on its side. All fish belonging to the flounder or flatfish group pass through the same peculiar changes during their development, so that their eyes eventually lie very close together. When the young flatfish hatches, it is a normally formed fish with eyes on opposite sides of its head. After a short period of growth, however, the body becomes flatter, and one eye starts to move toward the top of the head, and continues to move until it reaches a position on the opposite side very close to the other eye. In most cases a definite twisting or turning of the head occurs at the same time. These fish lie on the floor of the ocean on their side and, when they swim, they swim on one side, watching for food above them.

Fighting Fish

According to an article written some time ago by a "widely traveled" person, sporting people in the Far East match Siamese fighting fish in separate glass containers. They place two jars side by side, and the two fish dash themselves against the glass trying to get together. This exciting combat continues until one of the fighters becomes so enraged that it literally explodes! But eyewitnesses of these encounters tell a somewhat different story.

The males are used for fighting, and when two fish are matched they are put in the same container. As the fighters approach each other, they display brilliant colors of red, blue and green, each one apparently trying to outshine the other. These preliminaries last for several seconds, after which one or both fish will suddenly launch an attack almost too quick for the eye to follow. They nip vigorously and may lock jaws and remain in this position for some time. The fighting continues until one of the fish is no longer able to fight, whereupon his opponent is declared the winner. The loser is usually removed before it is killed.

Siamese fighting fish are found in the natural state in Siam, parts of China and in the Malay Peninsula, and for many years they have been bred in Siam for their fighting qualities.

Despite the small size of these fish, which have a maximum length of about two and a half inches, their courage, fighting qualities and endurance are remarkable. Wild males are quite pugnacious and are more than willing to fight, but they usually quit within a few minutes. However, the best pedigreed stock that has been bred for fighting qualities has been known to continue the combat for as long as six hours.

How Dangerous Are Sharks?

There have probably been more stories told about sharks than about any other one group of fish, and most discussions have dealt with whether or not they will attack human beings. Even before the war there were a number of authentic instances of sharks attacking human beings, but some biologists were nevertheless not convinced. Although attacks by sharks are relatively rare, in 1916 four persons were killed by sharks off the coast of New York and New Jersey. During World War II the Armed Forces of the United States considered the hazard from sharks so important that they developed a chemical shark repellent. This material, in the form of a cake, was attached to life belts and lifeboats in a waterproof covering. When exposed to the water, the repellent diffuses about the swimmer and is reported to repel sharks for two to four hours.

Although it is definitely known that some sharks are dangerous, many shark stories have been considerably exaggerated. There are about 150 different kinds of sharks, and of this number a very few account for most human casualties. These are the white shark or man-eater, the tiger shark, the blue shark and the hammerhead; but even they attack man only rarely and are less dangerous in some areas than in others, which perhaps is one reason for all the controversy regarding their appetites. The difference may be due to temperament, and also to the presence or absence of food in a given area. Where sharks are well fed from garbage or slaughterhouses, natives will frequently dive among them to recover coins, but where food is scarce no amount of money will tempt the divers into the water. Considering the number of exposures, we can be sure that no shark prefers a human being to all other articles of diet. Nevertheless, it is a wise person who heeds the warning, "Never trust any species of shark."

What Is the Most Dangerous Fish in the World?

Several kinds of fish, such as sharks and the barracuda, have earned the reputation of being dangerous, but none can compare in ferocity with some small freshwater fish of South America. These fish have various names including piranha, carabe and pirai. No land animal, however large, may be considered safe from these little balls of fury.

Observing a piranha in an aquarium, one gets no impression of the latent ferocity contained within that relatively small body. One sees a fish somewhat resembling a perch in general shape. But look closely at the large mouth with its pugnaciously protruding jaws. Observe that along the margin of each jaw are razor-sharp triangular-shaped teeth which seem too large for such a small fish.

Piranhas have the nasty habit of hunting in schools, and any animal that is attacked becomes the center of a seething maelstrom of activity until every shred of flesh has been ripped from its bones. It is reported that they sometimes turn savagely upon their fellows and devour them with equal relish. Several naturalists have written interesting accounts of experiences with the piranha, and many South American explorers, as well as natives, bear scars as a result of unpleasant encounters with them. One explorer, while fishing for piranhas, lost his balance and fell headfirst into a school of them. Before he gained the shore, only a short distance away, he was severely bitten in several places. Another naturalist reported that a native on muleback passed through the camp on his way home. A short time later the mule returned to camp, riderless. Following the mule tracks to a stream, the naturalist found the native's skeleton a short distance from the stream crossing, completely stripped of flesh. Piranha will fasten their razor sharp teeth upon the first part of the anatomy that comes within reach, and will continue their attack even out of water. Wooden planks and sticks will be chewed up with insatiable fury, and several men have had their fingers terribly mutilated when they attempted to remove a hook from a piranha's mouth.

Death-Dealing Rays

Sting rays, or stingarees, are very flat fish with a long whiplike tail near the base of which is a sharp jagged stinger. These fish have earned an evil reputation which is at least partially deserved, but the chances are that they are not deliberately vicious. They habitually lie partially buried in the sand and will naturally defend themselves if someone steps upon their backs. Their only weapon of defense is the long spine or stinger which they know too well how to use.

The jagged wound inflicted by the barb of a sting ray may be quite serious. Aside from the usual danger of infection, there is the fact that the barb releases into the wound a poison secreted by a gland connected to the spine. The effects of the sting frequently persist for weeks or months, and in some instances permanent injury to a limb has resulted. Tropical species are probably more dangerous than those found in temperate regions. I do not know of any cases of death from the sting of a stingaree in temperate regions, but some cases are known in tropical regions. Most sting rays are marine, but a freshwater species in the Amazon River seems to be about as dangerous as any. Richard Schomburgk, an early South American explorer, had several experiences with these fish. Two of his native helpers were stung by sting rays, and in both instances the men suffered excruciating pain and had violent convulsions. Although the wounds were treated at once, the lives of the men were saved only with difficulty. Several days later, Schomburgk was visiting at an estate when one of the laborers was stung, and although the man was young and vigorous he died in convulsions some time later. Other explorers have reported similar experiences.

Other fish that have dangerous venomous spines include the scorpion fish and the weaver fish. These have poison glands connected to spines along their backs, and a few persons have died as a result of stepping on them or handling them incautiously. Both these fish live in the ocean. There are many other fish that have venomous spines, but most of them are not dangerous to life. Common examples include the spiny dogfish, a marine form, and various catfishes that are found in both fresh and salt water.

Are Electric Eels Dangerous?

The electric eel inhabits the rivers and lakes of South America. It may attain a length of six to seven feet and is capable of delivering a very powerful electric shock. Doubtless many exaggerated stories have been related regarding the strength of the current generated by these fish, but some of the stories contain an element of truth. I do not know of anyone who has ever been killed directly by the shock of an electric eel, but some reported cases of death by drowning following an electric shock are very probably authentic.

Alexander von Humboldt, a South American explorer, wished to obtain some electric eels for experimental work, but he found that the natives feared them so intensely that he had to devise a special plan for catching them. A herd of horses was driven into a stream inhabited by electric eels in order to stir them up and thus facilitate their capture. The eels attacked the horses with discharges of electricity, and the horses plunged and reared wildly and made for the bank, only to be driven back into the water by the natives. During the confusion, a few eels came close enough to shore to be captured. When the horses were finally allowed to come ashore, they were hardly able to walk and two of them had drowned.

Another man saw a native boy who was swimming in a river suddenly shocked into insensibility by an electric eel. Only a prompt rescue by the boy's friends saved him from drowning, and the effects of the shock lasted for several hours. Many other naturalists and explorers have witnessed similar occurrences, and all agree that the electric eel is a potentially dangerous fish.

A Fish That Shocks Its Meal From Other Fish

In the Nile River of Africa there lives a fish called the electric catfish. Like the electric eel, it generates a current and, if we are to believe supposedly authentic reports, uses its electricity not simply for defense but to secure its food. It swims along until it discovers another fish in the process of digesting a meal, swims near and flicks on its current. The astonished victim vomits its meal in surprise and pain, and the catfish rapidly gobbles up the stuff.

Are Any Fish Poisonous to Eat?

A number of fish including the toadfish, the parrot fish, the porcupine fish, the puffers and the file- or triggerfish have poisonous flesh. Of this group, the most dangerous to eat are probably some of the toad and puffer fish which inhabit the waters near several South Pacific islands, and which have been responsible for many deaths, especially in Japan and adjacent areas. It has been claimed that the poisonous material is contained in the reproductive and digestive organs and that if they are quickly removed after the fish is killed it is not likely to be poisonous. Yet, Japanese, trusting in this belief, have marketed the fish alive and still many people have died from eating them. Even cooking these fish does not make them safe to eat, since heat does not destroy the poison.

Fortunately, the most dangerous species may be avoided by the application of a very simple rule: never eat a fish that does not look like a fish. This statement, stupid as it may sound, is essentially good advice. Very few poisonous fish have the usual fish form, but are frequently odd or even ugly in appearance. Puffers blow up their bodies with air or water; some species have spines rather than scales; while another has a hard bony beak resembling that of a parrot. All poisonous fish are marine—so far as known, there is no freshwater fish with poisonous flesh.

Do Eels Jump About in the Pan While Cooking?

It is probably the snakelike form of the eel that causes many people to regard this interesting species with distaste. There are a number of different kinds of eels, many of which live in salt water, but much to the disgust of feminine "Isaac Waltons" there are also freshwater eels, some of which may be caught occasionally on hooks. It is said that when eels are being cooked they will jump about in the frying pan, and I had one enthusiastic person tell me that he once had to tie on the lid of a frying pan to prevent the eel from jumping out onto the floor! This story was certainly an exaggeration, unless the man was talking about a live eel. I have seen pieces of a freshly killed eel move slightly in a pan, and the muscles quiver in the hot grease, but in most instances these movements are not noticeable unless one is watching for them. The movements are caused by muscular contractions, and they may also occur when one is cooking other kinds of meat, such as frogs' legs.

The flesh of eels is, of course, not poisonous, and the creatures do not have a poisonous bite. I have handled a fair number of freshwater eels and have yet to be bitten by one.

Can It Rain Fish?

From time immemorial this question has been discussed, and there have been numerous instances reported of fishes' falling with the rain. One of the most recent I have noted was said to have occurred in England in 1928. According to the story, a man left his house just after a rain and was amazed to find dozens of very small red fish in his yard and on the roof of the house. It was thought probable that the fish had been caught up in a waterspout from the sea some two miles away. The most recent discussion of this question I have seen took the form of a controversy between two men, one believing and the other disbelieving that fish fall with the rain. Both men presented their views in published articles in 1946, with the result that each holds the same opinion that he held before the argument started.

Most biologists who have investigated the matter believe that under certain conditions fish may fall with rain, but, so far as I know, such a phenomenon has never been observed by a trained naturalist. If it can rain fish, a possible explanation may be as follows: Whirlwinds swoop down over lakes or other bodies of water, and as they rise they may take up some water containing fish. The fish will drop eventually, but they may be carried for some distance before being "rained" upon astonished human beings. Most of the reports of raining fish come from coastal areas, but some have originated some distance inland. I personally shall keep an open mind upon the subject until additional evidence is brought forth.

Can Fish Drown?

Under the right conditions, many fish can drown just as surely as can a man. Fish breathe by taking oxygen from the water; if the oxygen in a body of water is used up, the fish must either move out of the area, obtain oxygen from some other source, or die of suffocation. Since drowning is caused by a lack of oxygen, a fish that dies in the water from this lack may accurately be said to have drowned. During the summer months in deep lakes in the middle-western part of the United States and similar areas, the oxygen at the bottom is all used up by animal respiration and by the decay of vegetation. Consequently, large numbers of fish die in these lakes when they do not

move out of the oxygenless region. The respiratory system of some fish that get out on land, such as the climbing perch, has become so modified that the creatures must obtain some of their oxygen from the air. A climbing perch forced to remain in water will drown shortly, no matter how much oxygen is present.

Can Fish Freeze and Still Live?

The ability of fish to withstand freezing conditions is dependent upon a number of factors, the most important probably being the kind of fish involved. It has been established that some fish can be frozen in solid ice and still survive, while other species will die even before freezing temperatures are reached. A biologist has described freezing solid some mud minnows with which he was experimenting. The ice broke the jar in which the fish were kept, but after they were thawed out they swam about as though nothing had happened.

The champion survivor of freezing is the blackfish found in Alaska and Siberia. Frequently it stays frozen for several months during the winter and, when the ice thaws in the spring, is apparently none the worse for the experience. Frozen blackfish are often used for feeding dogs. Occasionally a hungry dog swallows a fish whole, to be considerably embarrassed a short time later when the fish thaws out in his stomach. Usually he regurgitates it. If placed in water, the fish would in all probability swim unconcernedly away.

What Are Sardines?

Sardines are sardines only when they are safely in the can. According to the United States Bureau of Fisheries, sardines are any of the small fish that belong to the herring family. Different species are emphasized by the sardine industry in different parts of the world. Off the coast of California, most of the fish that are caught are the so-called California sardine, while in Maine the fishermen collect the sea herring. The canneries of France and Portugal can young pilchards, and in Norway the sprat receives the lion's share of attention. Some of the fish that are used as sardines have the scientific name *Sardina*, and it is probable that the common name of sardine derives from this.

Are Dogfish Edible?

I have not had the privilege of eating dogfish, but those who have tried it tell me that the flesh has a strong taste of ammonia. Apparently the flesh needs special treatment to be palatable.

The flesh of the dogfish has appeared on the menus of many restaurants and on the tables of people throughout the world, but not under the name of dogfish. In Canada and the United States we have "grayfish," in England it is "flake," while the name "sea eel" is used in Germany. In all cases, it is our old friend the dogfish parading under an assumed name.

Dogfish are well known to, but not popular with, fishermen who happen to snare them in their nets. The chances are that the net will be chewed up in several places before the pugnacious fish can be removed. Several species of dogfish occur in oceans throughout the world, and in some areas there are so many that organized attempts have been made to reduce their numbers to prevent them from destroying food fish. They are closely related to sharks and, when adult, are about two and a half to three feet in length.

Could the Largest Fish Have Swallowed Jonah?

The whale shark, although it is the largest living fish, is not a man-eater, and couldn't be even if it so desired. Its teeth are very small, only about an eighth of an inch in length, and its throat is only some four inches in diameter. People who have the idea that it was the whale shark that swallowed Jonah must thus revise their opinion. This colossal fish actually feeds upon some of the smallest creatures of the ocean, including sardines and small squids. Very little is known of its habits, since, as of 1938, only eighty to eighty-five specimens had been recorded, and many of these were relatively small.

Competent authorities have estimated that the whale shark may attain a length of sixty to seventy feet, but the largest specimen ever actually measured was only forty-five feet. This fish was caught near the Seychelles Islands off the West African coast about 1870. Another fish of approximately thirty-eight feet was reported to weigh 26,594 pounds.

A Fish That Saws Its Food

The sawfish feeds principally upon other fish. When it sights a school of fish, it swims into their midst, lashing back and forth with its wicked-looking saw and leaving a trail of dead and dying fish in its wake. When it has tired of this sport, it returns and leisurely devours as many of its victims as it can, leaving the remainder for other hungry denizens of the sea. The sawfish is quite willing to attack large fish or even whales. After lacerating its victim so severely that part of the insides are exposed, the sawfish swims along and feeds upon the torn flesh and trailing entrails. Sawfish are not entirely confined to salt water and have been known to go some distance up a river and attack human swimmers. It has even been reported that in parts of India sawfish have attacked human beings and cut them completely in two with their jagged weapon. I have not entirely confirmed these reports, but it is certain that a sawfish could inflict terrible wounds.

The young are born with the saw well developed, but at the time of birth the saw is encased in a sheath which prevents injury to the mother.

Sawfish are among the largest of fish. Specimens have been reported which were twenty-seven to twenty-nine feet long and weighed approximately 4500 pounds.

Some people have the impression that the swordfish and sawfish are quite similar, but actually they are very different. The sword of the swordfish is sharp, and smooth along the sides, while the saw of the sawfish is blunt on the end, flattened, and has large teeth along each edge. In addition the sawfish, which is related to the sting rays, is a rather flattened species, whereas the swordfish is compressed from side to side as are most fish.

The weapon of the swordfish is its upper jaw, which has become elongated into a sharp swordlike structure three or more feet in length. When young swordfish first hatch, they do not have a sword, but it develops rapidly as they grow. These fish feed upon other fish. Large species they may spit with the sword; small fish they procure by swimming into a shoal and striking rapid blows from side to side. Swordfish sometimes attack such large creatures as whales and sharks and usually emerge victorious. They are among the swiftest-swimming fish in the ocean and a clumsy whale is quite helpless against their flashing attacks.

Monster Parents With Midget Children

Ocean sunfish are very large, but their eggs and newborn young are astonishingly small. The eggs, which are only about one twentieth of an inch in diameter, hatch into small fish one tenth of an inch in length. These tiny atoms grow into adults which may be over eight feet long and weigh more than 1200 pounds. It has been estimated that the young sunfish must increase its weight approximately 60,000,000 times before it can attain the maximum size for the species. There is probably a greater size difference between the young and adult of ocean sunfish than between the young and adult of any other animal. Even the difference in size between the young and adults of the kangaroos and opossums, great as it is, shrinks into insignificance by comparison.

What Is the Largest Freshwater Fish?

It is generally thought that the largest freshwater fish is the arapaima or piraruca of the rivers of South America. This fish is said to reach a length of fifteen feet and a weight of 500 pounds. However, there are several kinds of sturgeons that are much larger than the arapaima. Some of them spend most of their time in fresh water, while others come into fresh water only to spawn. The largest of the sturgeons is the huso or giant Russian sturgeon. There is an established weight of 3221 pounds for one of these fish, and a length of up to twenty-six feet has been reported. Other large fish such as sharks and sawfish occasionally get into fresh water, but they do not spend as much of their time there as do the sturgeons. There are several species of catfish, wholly freshwater species, that also rival or exceed the size of the arapaima. One of the largest of these is the wels of European rivers. This fish is said to attain a length of fifteen feet and a weight of over 700 pounds, but I have not been able to confirm these figures.

Several very valuable fish products are obtained from sturgeons, and for this reason they have been caught so extensively that large specimens are now exceedingly rare. The product most in demand is obtained from the eggs or roe. These are treated and sold as caviar, a dish "fit for a king," but suspiciously resembling shot in appearance.

What Is the Smallest Vertebrate Animal?

Very few anglers vie with each other in attempts to catch the smallest fish, but these smaller creatures are just as interesting as the giants. As opposed to the possible sixty- or seventy-foot length of the whale shark which is the largest fish, the smallest fish must be measured in fractions of an inch. The smallest fish in the world are found in lakes in the Philippine Islands. There are several species that belong to the goby group, the largest of which measures only half an inch, and the smallest, called *Pandaka pygmaea*, only slightly more than a quarter of an inch.

These fish are the smallest living animals with a backbone, but despite their small size they are an important article of food in some parts of the Philippine Islands. They occur in such enormous numbers in some lakes that they are collected by the thousands and cooked into a concoction that is flavored with peppers and spices.

A Fish That Shoots Its Food

Of all methods of obtaining food, that used by the archer fish of India is easily the strangest. This fish feeds upons insects that live along the banks of streams and ponds. When it sees an insect hovering near the water surface or perched on an overhanging branch, it swims slowly until near its prey and carefully raises its mouth close to the water surface. Then—Sput!—and a drop of water is shot from the fish's mouth with unerring accuracy, strikes the insect and knocks it into the water where the fish can get it. The archer fish are surprisingly accurate at a distance of three or four feet, and some observers say that they have brought down prey at a distance of six feet. Within recent years some of these fish have become available as aquarium exhibits, and many of them will display their marksmanship in captivity.

Can a Swordfish Sink a Boat?

There have been numerous reports of swordfish that attack ships, even causing small craft to sink. The reasons for their attacks are not clear, but it is probable that they mistake the ships for whales or some other living animal that is invading their domain. The velocity attained by an attacking swordfish must be tremendous, for the sword is sometimes so deeply embedded in the wood that the fish is unable to withdraw it, and breaks it off in its attempts to escape. In a museum in England there is part of the bow of a ship into which a swordfish stuck its sword thirteen and a half inches deep through solid wood; and in the British Museum there is an exhibit of a timber from the side of a ship through which a swordfish's sword has penetrated for no less than twenty-two inches! Even human beings are not immune from these gladiators of the sea. Men have received severe wounds, and in 1830 off the coast of England, a man was killed by a swordfish.

Fish That Stand on Their Tails

Many people are familiar with sea horses, those little fish with horselike heads and nicely curled tails that usually swim about with their heads up. Because of the rather peculiar structure of the sea horse, this method of swimming does not seem so strange as it would for a fish with a more conventional shape.

Shrimp-fish or needlefish, as they are sometimes called, are small minnowlike fish with long snouts, found in the Indian Ocean. These fish have the habit of swimming in small schools, their tails down and their long snouts pointing upward. They have been seen to swim in the usual fishlike horizontal position, but when they do so, they are upside down.

There is a catfish found in the Nile River that looks very much like other catfish unless one happens to see it swimming bellyside up near the surface, a position not adopted by any other fish unless it is sick or dead.

How Long Do Fish Live?

It seems as though few people can talk or write about fish without exaggerating a little; and the champion fish story of all time, believed even by biologists for many years, concerned an ancient and hoary pike fish. This fish, according to the story, was caught in a lake in 1497, and attached to its body was a ring bearing an inscription to the effect that the fish had been put in the lake by the emperor, Frederick II. The aged fish, supposedly 267 years old, was thereafter called the Emperor's pike, and its skeleton was preserved in a German museum for many years. Its fame spread far and wide, and its great age was apparently accepted by many biologists, including Metchnikoff of the Pasteur Institute, who used it as an example of the longevity of fish. The bubble of its fame exploded with considerable repercussion, however, when a German anatomist, reverently studying the famous skeleton, found to his disgust that it was not a single skeleton at all, but was composed of the bones of several different fish!

Carp also have traditionally long lives. Buffon, a famous biologist, vouched for ages of as much as 150 years, but modern study shows that he was probably mistaken. The oldest verified age for a carp of which I could find a record was twenty-four years, but it is thought that some may live longer.

The species of fish with the greatest verified age record is the European catfish or wels. There is very good evidence that two of these fish have lived for over sixty years in a lake in England, and at the last report they were still alive. Eels, both European and American species, come in for their share of attention. The late Major Stanley Flower, an expert on animal ages, accepted ages of forty, forty-two and fifty-five for the European eel, and a probably fifty is listed for the American form. One of the European eels is of particular interest, because it was owned by a single family for more than forty years. A European sturgeon was kept for thirty-eight years in the Brighton aquarium, and even the lowly perch has been known to live for twelve years in the New York aquarium.

The fish with the shortest lives are doubtless some of the gobies. Most of these fish are quite small, and some species are frequently used as aquarium fish. Some of them might even be called "annuals," since they hatch, grow up, reproduce and die all within a single year. These fish, and possibly the ice fish of China, are the only vertebrate animals known with this type of life history; they thus have the dubious honor of being shorter lived than any other known vertebrate animal.

What Are Lampreys and Hagfish?

Lampreys and hagfish are elongated fishlike creatures which grow to a length of two or three feet and resemble eels. They are similar to fish and are called fish by most people, but they differ in so many important respects that biologists have classified them as a separate group called cyclostomes. One of the most noticeable differences is that cyclostomes do not have any limbs at all. The only fins they have are along the center of the back and tail, and on the under surface of the body near the rear end. Their skin is entirely scaleless, and skin glands secrete so much slime that it is almost impossible for a person to hold a cyclostome in his hands. Lampreys are found in both fresh and salt water, but hagfish are wholly marine.

Fish That Cannot Close Their Mouths

The mouth of the lamprey and the hagfish puts them high on the list of nature's oddities. Instead of having jaws, the mouth is surrounded by a band of cartilage. The creatures are thus doomed to swim through life with their mouths always open. However, the circular mouth is a very efficient sucker with which they can attach themselves to rocks and stones and even to other fish.

Most of the cyclostomes that live in fresh water do not

eat at all during their adult stages and consequently are never taken on hooks. An occasional specimen is caught in a net or trap, much to the horror of fishermen, many of whom believe that the fish are venomous. The creatures are not venomous, and since they do not have jaws it is improbable that they are capable of injuring human beings. During the Middle Ages, lampreys were in demand as food, especially among the nobility, and it has been said that Henry the First of England died as a result of eating too many. Today, however, they are seldom eaten.

What Fish Can Climb Up Cliffs?

Many marine lampreys come into fresh water to breed and, as they go upstream, sometimes encounter waterfalls too swift for easy swimming. Faced with such an obstacle, the lampreys use their suckerlike mouths to advantage. Attaching themselves to rocks to hold themselves against the current, they gradually work their way toward the falls by swimming forward short distances and again attaching to rocks nearer the falls. To climb a perpendicular cliff and enter the stream above the falls, as they sometimes do, the lamprey attaches its sucker to the cliff, wiggling its body vigorously and inching the sucker upward at the same time. At times they may be entirely out of the water. Huge numbers of them have been seen either anchored near the foot of falls or laboriously climbing over them.

When lampreys swim up a river to lay their eggs, they search for a place where the current is relatively slow. There they construct a crude nest of stones which they collect and move into place with their efficient mouths.

The person who first called these creatures lampreys must have observed this habit, for the name means "to lick rocks."

Parasitic Fish

A few species of lampreys normally feed upon small organisms such as worms, insects and various other forms of water life, but most marine lampreys and all hagfish are parasitic upon fish. This is worthy of notice because parasitism is rarely found among vertebrate animals. A lamprey usually remains on the outside of its victim's body, attached to it by means of its sucker, which works somewhat like a rubber suction disc. Once firmly attached, the parasite bores a hole in its host's body with its horny toothed tongue and allows the blood and body fluids to flow into its mouth. Lampreys usually do not kill their victims directly, but change hosts from time to time. The wounds they make, however, are likely to become infected, which often leads to the death of the fish. In some areas, lampreys constitute a major problem because they attack large numbers of important food fishes.

The feeding habits of the lamprey would present a problem if it had to get its oxygen from the water as most fish do by allowing the water to flow into its mouth, over the gills and out through the gill slits. If it had to release its grip on a fish to take water into its mouth, it would find that its meal had run away while it was breathing. The gills of the lamprey, however, lie in pouches in its body, and during respiration they expand and contract, drawing water into the gill slits and expelling it at the same place.

The hagfish as a rule is not satisfied merely to attach

itself to the outside of another fish. It usually bores its way right into the body of its victim and, working from the inside, eventually consumes almost the entire fish. Fishermen frequently net large fish that are nothing but a skinful of bones, with a well-fed hag complacently reposing within.

Do Freshwater Fish Ever Breed in the Ocean?

That some marine fish, such as the salmon, enter fresh water to breed is a fairly well-known fact, but many people do not know that a few freshwater fish reverse the process. Perhaps it is appropriate that the freshwater eel, a creature about which many fish stories are told, should be one exception to the general rule.

Freshwater eels become mature when several years old and shortly thereafter start downstream toward the ocean. Huge numbers congregate in a common breeding ground in the Atlantic Ocean, south and southwest of Bermuda. Here the adults spawn and, having performed their parental duties, die within a short time. The egg hatches, not into a respectable-looking eel, but into a curious flattened leaflike creature called a larval eel. Biologists were familiar with this larva long before its connection with the adult eel was established, but it differs so radically from the adult that it was regarded as a different kind of fish. Some biologist gave these larvae the scientific name of *Leptocephalus*, and now that they are known to be immature eels they are frequently called leptocephalus larvae. The larvae eventually find their way back to shore, but before they can enter fresh water they must change into another larval form called an elver. The elvers swim

Animal Facts *and* Fallacies

up the streams and remain in fresh water until they become mature.

Curiously enough, the American and European eels, although different species, use the same general breeding grounds; sometimes even intermingling. Yet the two species remain distinct, and an American eel has never been found in European waters or vice versa. It is quite possible that the larvae may ocasionally make a mistake and swim off in the wrong direction, but if they do it is unlikely that they live to boast of their travels. The reason lies in their different rates of development. The larva of the American eel takes only a year to develop into an elver, but the European form takes about three years to attain this same stage. It takes approximately the same time for each species to reach its respective home land. If the larva of an American eel were to swim toward Europe, it would find itself in the embarrassing position of changing into an elver in the middle of the ocean, two thousand miles or so from shore. European larvae wandering toward the American continent would arrive a couple of years before they had reached the stage where they were ready to live in fresh water. During the waiting period, the chances would be very much against the survival of the infant Europeans.

[168]

PART FOUR

Amphibians

What Are Amphibians?

Frogs, toads, salamanders and similar creatures are amphibians. They lack the scaly covering of reptiles, their skin being relatively naked and, in many species, moist and slimy. The term amphibian means double life, indicating that many of these animals lead both a water and a land existence. Most amphibians hatch from eggs laid in water, and live in water throughout the larval stage, breathing through gills. The gills are eventually supplanted or supplemented by lungs, which enable the adults to live on land, although some amphibians spend all their lives in water.

What Is the Difference Between Frogs and Toads?

Both frogs and toads have long hind legs and, as adults, are completely tailless. Frogs, however, have a moist, relatively smooth skin and are agile jumpers; toads give clumsy short hops and their skin is rough, warty and dry. In places where there are only a few species of each, as in parts of the United States and northern Europe, it is not difficult to distinguish between the two forms, but in

some regions the line of demarkation between these two types of jumping amphibians is not so distinct. The term frog is acceptable when speaking of the frog and toad group in general.

Why Do Frogs Die in Dry Air?

Frogs spend part of their time on land, but they never venture far from water, for if they do not have a moist environment they will die. The reason is that the evaporation of the body fluids through the skin is so rapid that the frog must replace these fluids by periodically soaking itself in water. I have seen a leopard frog, a species frequently used in biology classes, die within twelve hours because it was kept out of water. All amphibians lose a certain amount of water through the skin, but the rough-skinned toads lose it less quickly than the smooth-skinned frogs. Consequently toads, with their thicker skins, are often found some distance from water.

An Amphibian With Two Forms

The name axolotl was first given to a dark, yellow-spotted, gilled salamander found in some lakes around Mexico City. At the time it was named, it was thought that the creature spent all its life in the water and it was considered to be a normal species of salamander until around 1865. About this time, several specimens were received in a zoological garden in Paris. Shortly after their arrival, an interesting series of events occurred. The axolotls mated; laid eggs which duly hatched into small gilled salamanders—thus far all normal enough. Then a peculiar thing happened. Some of the young axolotls lost their gills, underwent a few other changes and came out on land. Study revealed that these transformed axolotls were simply tiger salamanders, identical with or similar to a species common in many parts of the United States. But the disappointment the zoo director and his staff may have experienced in seeing a valuable exhibit transform into a very common species was more than compensated for by the intensely interesting discovery that the axolotl was actually the larval form of a well-known salamander. The most amazing part of the whole discovery, of course, was the fact that under other environmental conditions these immature forms actually reproduced. In some regions, that is, the sexual organs of the axolotl become mature and capable of reproduction, though it retains all the other features of the larval forms. In other regions—and this is what happened in the Paris Zoo—the larvae develop into tiger salamanders and come out on land before they reproduce. The process of reproduction in the larval form is so seldom encountered that it makes the axolotl one of the most amazing vertebrates in the whole animal kingdom.

A Field Full of Sirens

In amphibian circles the name siren is not applied to a fascinating and dangerous female of the human species, but to a very peculiar group of salamanders. These snakelike creatures, which may grow to be three feet long, have gills just behind the head, and only one pair of legs. Normally, they spend all their lives in the water, but if the swamp or stream in which they live dries up they burrow into the mud and are able to survive even though the ground becomes quite dry. When the ground becomes wet again, they emerge from their burrows none the worse for their experience.

A farmer, once, during a drought, had his son plow a dried-up swamp. After the boy had been working for a short time, he came running to the house in great excitement and gasped that the field was full of snakes. The farmer went to the field, fearfully accompanied by his son, and saw to his consternation that the plow had indeed unearthed a number of creatures greatly resembling snakes. They were not very active; so the man gingerly collected one in a bucket and departed for town to have it identified. The biology teacher at the school told him that the snake-like animal was a siren, and quite harmless. When placed in water the farmer's specimen shortly became very active and was soon swimming about, its small front legs clearly visible. Convinced at last that his son had not discovered a field of poisonous snakes, the farmer returned home and with some difficulty persuaded the boy to continue his interrupted task. Several hundred sirens were uncovered before the swampy area was completely plowed.

Are Mudpuppies Poisonous?

These salamanders, also called water dogs and various other less-complimentary names, are often said to be capable of giving a person a painful nip. Although I have caught numbers of them barehanded, I have never been bitten by one, nor do I know of anyone else who has. Whether they bite or not, they are definitely not venomous, although many fishermen are intensely afraid of them.

Once these salamanders have been identified, they are easily recognized in the future, for they have three pairs of gills just behind the head. In a live salamander, the gills are bright red and move back and forth in the water as the salamander rests on the bottom of the pond or stream, or walks slowly among the rocks. The legs are well developed and the body is usually reddish brown with darker splotches scattered over the surface. Its food consists chiefly of worms and similar organisms, and it will frequently seize a hook baited with them. In some regions, they may be caught in large numbers.

Another salamander, also frequently caught by fishermen, is the hellbender; and in view of its ugly appearance it is appropriately named. It is somewhat similar to the mudpuppy, but it is larger, does not have the fluffy gills behind the head, and its skin is extremely wrinkled. Despite its formidable and hideous appearance, it is not venomous; indeed, there is no salamander known that has a poisonous bite. Inasmuch as I have not had the privilege of catching hellbenders barehanded, I cannot speak from personal knowledge of their biting ability, but some biologists say that they can administer a rather vicious bite.

Frogs That Fly

In Borneo, Java and adjacent areas there are some tree frogs that have unusually large feet with webbed toes. For many years these frogs have been said to be capable of making prodigious leaps from trees, the spread of their webbed feet supposedly enabling them to glide much further than they otherwise could. In a description of their flight or glide published in 1915, it was said that one frog was seen to jump from a tree and land some thirty to forty yards away. Their ability to make tremendous leaps is now fully accepted, but some biologists contend that the large membranes of their feet are of no material help, that the frog could jump just as far without them.

South America has a flying tree frog which apparently does as well without webs as the more famous flying frog of the big feet. One observer performed a large number of experiments with this species. When he tossed the frog into the air, it quickly righted itself, flattened its body and landed on the ground unhurt, belly side down. When he made the frog leap from a tower 140 feet high, it jumped, flattened its body and glided some ninety feet before it came to the ground. This same observer found that European frogs of comparable size fell vertically and made no attempt to orient themselves so that they would land on their bellies and feet. More observations are needed, but at the present time there seems to be little doubt that certain species of frogs have some ability to glide.

A Toad That Uses Its Back as an Incubator

In parts of South America there is a peculiar tongueless amphibian called the Surinam toad—one of the few tailless amphibians to spend all its life in the water. It is a curious flattened creature about five inches in length, with several projections arranged in the shape of a star on each toe of the front feet. Although the appearance of this amphibian is extraordinary enough to invoke comment, its reproductive habits are even more remarkable. At the time of mating, the male scrambles upon the back of the female and clasps her tightly. The eggs are then expelled from a tube which protrudes from the end of the female's body and arches over her back under the belly of the male.

Amphibians

The male presses the eggs into little pouches in the female's back, where they are held by a sticky secretion. There they remain, covered by a gelatinous lid, until development is completed. When the young finally push the tops from their prisons and emerge into the outside world, they are tiny toads and not tadpoles.

A Male Frog That Makes a Nest of Its Vocal Pouches

The males of many species of frogs and toads have a pair of small vocal sacs or pouches which open into the mouth. Their principal use is to increase the volume of the voice. When the frogs croak, the sacs become greatly distended with air; at other times they are not noticeable. One group of cricket frogs in South America, whose pouches open from the floor of the mouth, has found a unique use for them—they carry the eggs in these sacs. During the incubation period, the pouches become so enlarged that they extend well over the undersurface of the body. The embryos remain in the pouches until they have completed their development and emerge as small frogs.

How Did the Midwife Toad Get Its Name?

In southwestern Europe there is a small toad that has been given the name of midwife or obstetrical toad. However, it is the male of the species whose services are utilized in caring for the eggs. He gets his hind legs entangled in the strings of eggs and then goes into hiding. Occasionally he ventures forth at night to feed, and moistens the eggs in the water. Eventually he goes into the water and stays there until all the eggs have hatched. After this, he is again able to take his place in amphibian circles, unencumbered by entangling strands of developing young.

Can Toads Live For Years Sealed in Solid Rock?

Every now and then newspaper headlines inform a receptive public that a toad has been found in a small chamber sealed in solid rock. The article is frequently supported by a statement from some "expert" in biology, such as the local mayor, that the animal must have been entombed for at least a hundred years.

As far as biologists are concerned, this question was settled as early as 1777; nevertheless in 1825 William Buckland of Oxford University, England, performed additional experiments. He took twenty-four toads, placed twelve of them in small cells in nonporous sandstone, and the other twelve in cells in porous limestone, sealed them all in their cells and buried them at a depth of three feet. At the end of a year, all the cells were opened. The toads that had been entombed in the nonporous sandstone were all dead, but most of those in the porous limestone were alive. It is thought probable that the living toads were able to survive because the porous walls of their chamber had allowed a certain amount of air to reach them, and may have also permitted an occasional insect to get in. The toads were again buried and left for another year, but when examined the second time they were all dead. Buckland also put toads in holes in trees and sealed them up, but all died within less than a year. His experiments prove that it is impossible for toads to live for any great length of time completely sealed or buried, although their survival for more than a year is itself quite remarkable.

It is certainly true that toads are sometimes found in the ground, or apparently sealed within rocks. However, people do not go out looking for entombed toads specifically, and to come upon one accidentally they must have at least partly destroyed the toad's chamber, making it impossible to determine how hermetically it was enclosed. The chances are that passages existed large enough to allow the toad to come and go as he chose, or at least large enough for insects to get in and keep him supplied with food.

Does the Toad Have a Venomous Bite?

About 1892, a famous naturalist published an interesting book in which he described a South American barking or horned toad that was supposed to have a very poisonous bite. He gave two instances in which a dead horse had been found with the jaws of the toad still fastened to it, the conclusion being, of course, that death was due to the bite of the toad. The horned or barking toads are probably the most aggressive and vicious amphibians in existence, but their bite is not venomous. They have, however, a very ugly disposition and definitely resent any intrusion upon their privacy. When annoyed, they usually puff up their bodies with air, and if given half a chance they will attack. Since the teeth in some species are quite well developed, they can inflict a rather serious wound. Once one of these toads has clamped its jaws on an enemy it holds on with bulldog tenacity, and it is almost impossible to break its grip without killing it.

Most of the larger amphibians will bite under some

conditions, including the hellbender, the congo eel, and various other large species of salamanders, frogs and toads. There is no amphibian known, however, that has a venomous bite.

Can Toads Kill Dogs?

Many readers have probably seen their dogs catch toads and then almost immediately drop them, frequently frothing at the mouth. I have watched this happen many times,

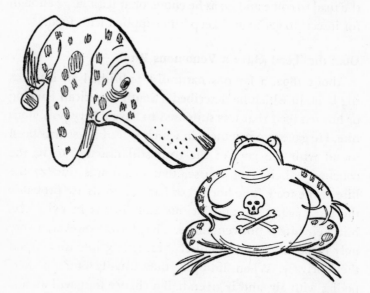

but I have never seen a dog succeed in eating the toad, although some are quite persistent in trying. If a dog were to be successful, it would be quite unhappy a short time later, for in the toad's warty skin are a large number of glands which secrete a powerful poison. This poison is so irritating to the dog's mouth that it usually drops the toad

[180]

immediately. A large dose of this skin poison may be fatal, and there is enough in a single toad either to kill a small dog or make it violently ill.

In some species this poison is considerably more powerful than it is in the common toad. Indians of South America use the secretion from the skin of a tree frog as a poison for the tips of their arrows, and, although I do not know of any experiments with the substance, a single frog is said to secrete enough to supply fifty arrows. The skin of this tree frog is also used to color the feathers of parrots artificially. Some of the normal green feathers are plucked out and the frog is rubbed over the bird's skin. When the new feathers grow in, they are yellow instead of green. People have succumbed to the lure of a brilliant green and yellow parrot only to find that when the feathers were shed they grew back green instead of yellow.

Some Frogs Eat Alligators

Several species of large frogs and toads will eat practically any living thing they can catch and overpower, including other frogs, small mammals and birds. The American bullfrog has been known to swallow young water birds, and the barking frog of South America catches mice, birds and similar creatures. The giant South American toad, with a body length of seven to eight inches, is probably the largest of the toads, and one of them holds what must be the championship for gastronomic ability in the toad clan. According to a story, several South American toads were received at a university for experimental purposes. Because of lack of space, the toads were placed in a cage with two young alligators about eleven inches long, where they all lived in harmony for several days. A week or so later, when it was decided to separate the toads and alligators, one of the alligators was unaccountably missing. Intensive search failing to turn it up, the toads came under suspicion, and all of them were subjected to X-rays. Sure enough, the missing alligator was discovered coiled within the stomach of one of the toads.

Dr. Frank Blair of the University of Texas supports the above story with one of his own that is even better. In this case a bullfrog with a body length of only about five inches and an alligator ten or eleven inches long were involved. The two were in the same cage, and one morning the alligator had disappeared, while the frog looked suspiciously distended and was quite inactive. The body of the alligator could be felt within the frog's body. The frog eventually recovered, but was not very active for several days.

Do Toads Cause Warts?

The cause-and-effect relationship between toads and warts is traditional. Some people believe that simply the touch of the toad's skin is sufficient to cause warts to develop, while others think that it is the toad's urine which produces them. However, toads never cause warts, although it is easy to see how this idea originated. As previously noted, most toads secrete an irritating and poisonous substance which in some species may actually burn or irritate the skin of anyone who handles them incautiously. Also many frogs and toads have a tendency to urinate when they are seized, and if the urine gets into a broken place in the skin it produces a burning sensation. But neither the poison nor the urine causes warts.

A Toad Horde

Most amphibians hibernate during the winter. The quarters selected vary with the different kinds of amphibians, but toads usually burrow into soft earth and remain there until spring. Upon emerging from hibernation, many species immediately mate and deposit the eggs in water, frequently descending upon the rivers and lakes in hordes. Several years ago, I was fortunate in seeing such a mass emergence on a river in central Texas. Dr. D. B. Casteel of the University of Texas, a biologist wise in the ways of toads, had agreed to take me to the river at the proper time. Near the end of February, the weather became warm for several days, and the toad expert decided that the toad season was at hand. Consequently, several of us drove to the river one night, stopped the car motors and turned out the lights. We were greeted by a chorus of male love songs which indicated that our guide had selected the proper time. As we approached the river, there in the glare of the flashlights were toads, seemingly millions of toads. There were toads in the shallow water, there were toads along the bank, and for some distance back from the water the ground appeared to be hopping with toads—all headed for the river. There seemed to be all types: medium-sized toads, small, runty, male toads and great waddly female toads with their bodies almost bursting with eggs. We collected over 1100 of them within two hours, which gives some indication of how many there were.

A sight such as this can be seen in many areas if the

proper time is selected. The first warm spell in the spring, particularly if accompanied by rain, will usually bring the toads from their hibernating quarters. They continue to emerge for a week or so, primarily at night, and after the eggs are laid they scatter over the countryside in search of food.

What Is the Largest Amphibian?

The largest amphibian is the giant salamander, an entirely aquatic species, that is found in Japan and parts of China. It may attain a length of between five and six feet, and there is a record of five feet seven inches for a specimen caught in China. One captive giant salamander weighed eighty-eight pounds when alive and ninety-nine pounds after death, which indicates that the body probably absorbed water from the aquarium after the creature died. These salamanders inhabit swift mountain streams, subsisting upon fish, insects and worms. Formerly, the Japanese caught them in large numbers for food, and sometimes even used them for medicine. Recently, however, the government has given them protection to prevent their extinction.

The largest of the frog and toad group is the goliath frog, an enormous amphibian found in west Africa in the area known as the Cameroons. The body of this creature may reach a length of twelve or thirteen inches, and the legs may be longer than the body, so that its over-all length may be more than two feet. The natives use these giant frogs for food, and the large thighbones are much prized for use in ceremonial rites. Consequently, very few specimens have found their way into museum collections.

Amphibians

How Long Do Amphibians Live?

In my reading, I constantly come upon a reference to a fabulous toad that was supposed to have lived for thirty-six years. Usually its species is not indicated, but some authors manage to give the impression that it was an American toad. Actually, however, this legendary toad was a common toad of Europe which was supposed to have been in the possession of a single family for thirty-six years. The late Major Stanley Flower, an authority on animal ages, carefully investigated this case and considered the report accurate. It should be emphasized however, that, so far as is known, only one toad has ever attained this age; it is not routine procedure for toads, as it is sometimes intimated. The next authentic age record for toads and frogs is twenty years for a fire-bellied toad of Europe, and the best an American toad can boast of is a life of ten years.

As a rule, the larger species of amphibians live longer than the smaller forms; thus we find that the record is held by the largest amphibian of all, the giant Japanese salamander. The longest-lived for which there is definite record survived approximately fifty-two years in a zoological park in Leyden, Holland, and its age at death was believed to be about fifty-five years. Passing to other groups, we find a hellbender that lived for twenty-nine years, and a siren for twenty-five. An axolotl lived for twenty-five years in its larval form in Covent Garden, London, while in its adult stage one at Ann Arbor, Michigan, survived for eleven years. Even small tree frogs have been known to live for from seven to sixteen years, and the North American bullfrog, sometimes credited with living for thirty years, has an established record for sixteen years.

How Far Can Frogs Jump?

Frogs, with their well-developed hind legs, are able to make tremendous leaps. Even such small species as the cricket frog, whose body is only an inch long, can jump three feet, while the American bullfrog has the reputation of making leaps of eight to ten feet.

The famous Jumping Frog Jubilee of Angel's Camp, California, held in commemoration of Mark Twain's well-known story, is probably more fun than a three-ring circus. According to eyewitnesses of these contests, each frog is allowed three jumps, and the contestant that covers the greatest distance in the three jumps wins. The frogs' owners are allowed to punch each frog before the first jump, but not after this. Frequently the frogs are very un-co-operative. Some will sit contentedly for a time and then take waddly jumps of a few inches; others will not budge until the owners in disgust try to pick them up, at which point they will make a tremendous leap of six feet or so, with no regard for the sweating, swearing, pursuing human being.

The winning jump is sometimes disgracefully short. In 1929 the total of the three jumps for the winning frog was actually less than a foot. Sometimes the frogs exert more effort. According to one writer, the winner in the 1938 contest broke previous records with a total of fifteen feet ten inches for the three jumps.

Can Frogs Sing Under Water?

Since frogs normally sing with their mouths and nostrils closed, they are able to sing even under water, although the water somewhat deadens the sound.

Some time ago, I was walking along the edge of a pond when I was attracted by the croaking of a frog. The sound continued for about five minutes and, although I closely examined all possible hiding places along the edge of the pond, I could not find it. Suddenly, about ten feet from shore there was a furious splashing of water, and a large water snake rose to the surface holding a croaking frog in its mouth. They had both been under water all the time I was trying to locate the source of the noise.

The so-called singing or croaking of frogs and toads is almost entirely limited to the males, although some females may make sounds when they are injured or disturbed. The male seems to use its voice principally to attract the female, but some of them certainly sing when their minds are not on mating, for a clamor of amphibian voices can be heard at night in almost any swamp long after the mating season is past. To sing, the frog or toad inhales, closes its mouth and nostrils, and forces the air back and forth between the mouth and lungs. Sound is produced by the action of the air passing over the vocal cords and causing them to vibrate. Many species of frogs have vocal sacs opening into the mouth, which during singing become greatly distended with air. These distended sacs, acting as resonators, are sometimes so large compared to the size of the frog's body that the creature seems to be a large, rounded sac to which a small frog is attached. The American bullfrog has the loudest frog voice known; the bellowing of ardent males may sometimes be heard for a mile or even more.

Why Is a Frog's Tongue Attached in Front?

Many frogs and toads depend almost entirely upon their tongues for catching food. In these amphibians, the tongue is attached at the front end and free at its forked posterior end. When the frog spots a moving fly or similar creature, it flicks out its tongue, which is covered by a sticky substance, and the insect becomes hopelessly entangled.

This method of catching prey is doubtless quite efficient, else there would not be so many frogs and toads; but sometimes the frog, which is attracted by movement, makes a mistake. One afternoon near dusk I flicked a burning cigarette from the porch to the ground. A toad hopped lazily into view and, as I watched, it came gradually closer to the cigarette. Smoke still curled upward. Suddenly the toad changed direction and hopped over to the cigarette. It eyed the curling smoke a moment, and then quick as a flash flipped out its tongue; the still-burning cigarette disappeared down its gullet, and the toad hopped unconcernedly away! The amazing part of the whole affair is that it never showed the slightest sign of discomfort, although I watched until it was out of sight.

PART FIVE
Reptiles

What Are Reptiles?

Reptiles include snakes, lizards, crocodiles, alligators, turtles and a variety of similar creatures. They all have scales on their bodies, and some, like the alligators, also have large bony plates. They differ from birds and mammals in that they are cold blooded, a condition that causes the body temperature to vary with the temperature of the air. For this reason, reptiles that live in temperate regions must hibernate during the winter months or die.

It is unfortunate that so many people have a fear of reptiles, either real or affected, because in some ways these animals are the most interesting in the entire animal kingdom. The average person thinks that reptiles are slimy but, actually, the skin of all reptiles is very dry. The scales of some snakes and lizards shine when the sun strikes them, and it is this reflected light that sometimes makes the skin look wet.

Snakes Walk With Their Ribs X

Snakes have overcome the handicap of being legless and armless, and can crawl and swim; some species can even climb. Although most serpents do not break any speed records, some of the racers and whipsnakes can give a man a good race over rough ground. On the snake's belly there is a series of plates each of which is free at the rear edge and attached at the front edge to a movable rib. In leisurely crawling, the ribs and plates are moved forward and then back, progress being aided as the free rear edges of the plates catch on various rocks, sticks or other obstructions. Snakes are the only animals that actually walk with their ribs.

When a snake is really in a hurry, it wiggles its body from side to side, using rocks and uneven places in the ground to help push its body forward. A snake is usually quite helpless if placed on a slick surface such as a large piece of glass. Neither the plates nor the sides of the body are able to find purchase, and the snake flounders about helplessly.

Snake Eggs Will Bounce

Once, when a child, I was scratching under a log and discovered several elongated objects which I knew were eggs of some kind. Gathering them carefully, I presented them to a spinster aunt of mine, who exclaimed with horror that they were snake eggs and should be destroyed. Somewhat disappointed at having my discovery condemned, I decided to experiment with the eggs before destroying them. I found to my great pleasure that they bounced when I dropped them on soft ground, instead of breaking. They were not, however, elastic enough to withstand my enthusiasm, and too-vigorous bouncing brought the experiment to a sudden conclusion, to the relief of my aunt.

[192]

I was astonished to find inside each egg a miniature but well-formed snake; however, even these helpless embryos were trampled under my aunt's supervision.

Some snakes, such as rattlesnakes, copperheads and garter snakes, give birth to living young. In other species, the young are hatched from eggs, which are usually larger in relation to their diameter than are the eggs of chickens and birds. A rather tough elastic shell is characteristic of the eggs of most reptiles.

Do Snakes Bite With Their Tongues? X

All that a great many people know about snakes is that they have a forked flickering tongue with which—so the erroneous belief runs—they bite. However, a snake's tongue is quite soft and is incapable of inflicting injury of any kind. As the snake crawls about, its tongue darts in and out continuously, particularly when the snake's suspicion or interest is aroused. The tongue is a highly developed sense organ, used principally in touching and as an aid in smelling. It was at one time thought that it also helped to pick up sound vibrations, but this is now believed not to be true.

Is There a Snake That Stings With Its Tail?

Some time ago a friend of mine came into my office and asked if there was a snake that could sting with its tail. When I assured him that there was not, he was considerably relieved and told the following story. His son, aged ten, was in school and was taking his first course in science. The teacher had told the students a very interesting story about a stinging hoop snake. This particular snake, which had a long, poisonous stinger in its tail, amused itself by taking its tail in its mouth and rolling hooplike over the landscape. One day as the snake was rolling about the country side, it became very angry and looked about for something upon which to vent its wrath. Suddenly it saw a peach tree upon which there were a number of nice ripe peaches. The angry serpent immediately stung the tree and, having thus relieved its feelings, rolled away. Some hours later, so the story went, several people ate peaches from the tree and immediately died as a result of the poison in the peaches that had been injected into the tree by the snake!

My friend's son was somewhat more interested in biology than the other students in the class and he asked the teacher to help him learn more about this strange snake. She readily agreed to help him, but although biology books, encyclopedias and other reference books were combed from cover to cover no hoop or stinging snake could be found, to the embarrassment of the teacher who had apparently sincerely believed the story.

The hoop snake and stinging snake are sometimes considered to be two different snakes; in other stories they seem to have been combined into one. Actually these are local names for two kinds of snakes, commonly called mudsnakes, which are probably responsible for most of the stories. Both these snakes sometimes rest with their bodies in a partial circle, and even such a snake expert as the late Dr. Raymond Ditmars admitted that he had occasionally mistaken them for bicycle tires. Some people with a very good imagination have decided that any snake that rests in this way could undoubtedly take its tail in its mouth and roll from one place to another. However, no snake is capable of performing such an acrobatic feat. The mudsnakes have a small, hard spine at the tip of the tail, which they probably use in burrowing. Despite the fact that it is generally believed to be deadly poisonous, this spine is completely harmless.

Flying Snakes

There is no snake that can fly as do birds and bats, but there are several species that can glide to some extent. The best known of these "flying snakes" is the golden tree snake of Asia, the Dutch East Indies and adjacent areas. Several biologists have confirmed the gliding ability of this reptile. It spends much of its time in the trees and frequently progresses from one branch to another by a series of jumps. The late Major Stanley Flower saw one jump from a windowsill to the branch of a tree eight feet away, and it has been reported that they can successfully glide to the ground from rather tall trees. When the snake glides, it flattens its body, makes its belly concave and holds itself rigid so that it is shaped like a piece of split bamboo or cane.

The flying snake is not venomous, but naturalists who have observed it consider it one of the fiercest snakes in existence. It will usually attack rather than retreat, and it will bite fiercely until it is overcome. It feeds chiefly upon lizards, but has also been known to eat mice and similar creatures.

Animal Facts *and* Fallacies

Do Snakes Milk Cows?

Many farmers and others who own cattle seriously believe that there are snakes that milk cows, a practice upon which they frequently blame a decrease in milk production. The name of milk snake is applied to some of the king snakes which are widely distributed over the eastern and midwestern parts of the United States. These snakes are frequently found around barns where they feed upon rats and mice. They have been known to take milk from a pan that has been put out for pets, which is probably how the cow-milking story originated.

Quite aside from the fact that no biologist has ever seen a cow-milking snake, it would be physically impossible for a snake to milk a cow. Snakes have many sharp teeth, and it is difficult to imagine a cow stupid enough to stand quietly while its teats were being chewed up. And, as one biologist has remarked, the snake would not be able to reach the cow's udder unless it had brought along its own milking stool. If it were to try to wrap its body around the cow's leg to reach the teats, the cow would certainly object. Any farmer having a sharp decrease in milk production would be more apt to increase his yield by getting other cows than by killing all the snakes in the vicinity.

Does the Coachwhip Snake Whip Human Beings?

In some parts of the United States there is a popular belief that the coachwhip snake will attack a person by wrapping its body about him and administering a sound thrashing with the end of its tail. To add fuel to the story, the color pattern of its tail does resemble a plaited whip.

However, I have never talked to anyone who claimed to have seen this happen and, needless to say, biologists give no credence to the story.

The common name of coachwhip snake is applied to several varieties of snakes called racers, or whipsnakes.

Do Snakes Swallow Their Young For Protection?

This story has probably won wider acceptance than any other fact or fancy concerning snakes. Biologists who deny it are almost sure to be bombarded with uncomplimentary letters. Although I have no desire to increase my mail, I too must cast my lot with the unbelievers. No biologist, no matter how many snakes he has observed and studied, has ever seen a mother snake swallow its young. This story, despite the wide belief accorded it, must be regarded as simply another snake yarn.

It is unquestionably true, however, that many people have seen what they thought was a mother snake swallowing her young for protection; but they simply misinterpreted the snake's actions. Many snakes eat other snakes and lizards, and an inexperienced person, seeing a snake swallow the brood of another female snake, might well think he was seeing young snakes going into their mother's mouth for protection. Unfortunately, most untrained observers make no attempt to prove or disprove this obvious interpretation, although I have read of at least one man who did. While walking in the woods one day, he surprised a female snake with several young. The young snakes crawled rapidly to the female and disappeared, apparently down her throat. If the man had not investigated further, he would have believed to his dying day that he had seen a female snake swallowing her young. He captured the adult snake, but when she did not release the young after several hours he returned to the woods and examined the spot where he had found them. A brief search revealed the young snakes snugly reposing at the bottom of a hole in the ground. When he had first come upon the snakes the mother snake, while watching him, had placed her head over this hole, and all the young ones had crawled under her head into it. From a distance it had looked as though they were disappearing down her throat.

Is the Rattlesnake a Gentleman?

Two beliefs are current regarding the rattles of rattle-snakes. One is that the age of the snake can be determined by the number of rattles it has, since one and only one rattle is supposed to be added each year. The other belief is that the snakes have a code of honor much higher than that of human beings and always rattle before they strike.

Although a rattle is usually added each time the snake sheds its skin, this does not always happen. In any case, it is not much help in determining the age of a snake, because the number of times a snake sheds its skin depends upon the amount of food it gets to eat. It may not shed its skin at all, or it may shed it several times; two or three times a year is probably average. Also, rattles frequently break off, so that a large snake, several years old, might have only one or two.

Unfortunately for the romanticists, all rattlesnakes are not gentlemen (or ladies) and they do not always rattle before striking. When rattlesnakes become frightened or angry, they usually vibrate their tails rapidly, which causes the rattles to strike together and make a distinctive buzzing sound. During warm weather, when the snakes are not sluggish, the majority will probably rattle if given half a chance, but the practice is far from invariable. Dr. A. I. Ortenburger of the University of Oklahoma studied this habit among rattlesnakes in Arizona and found that only four per cent of those he collected rattled before they struck. While this high percentage of villains among the rattlesnake clan would probably not hold under all conditions, his experience does emphasize that a warning rattle cannot always be expected.

Do Snakes Charm Their Prey?

Snakes are not capable of charming human beings; if they were, snake collectors would very shortly become extinct. It is true that some people are so frightened when they see a snake that they are frozen immovable, but this reaction is not the same as being charmed or hypnotized. Most biologists do not believe that snakes can charm smaller animals any more than they can charm people, but it seems possible that some of the smaller creatures may likewise become so frightened that they do not move until it is too late. Birds are most commonly associated with the snake-charming story, but their occasionally peculiar behavior around snakes probably has another cause. Observers have frequently seen a mother bird fluttering dangerously near a snake's head, giving an impression of easy capture, until it has drawn the snake a safe distance from the nest. Then it miraculously recovers and flies safely away, doubtless to the chagrin of the hungry snake. Occasionally, however, a bird becomes too brave while trying to attract a snake's attention and is captured. Anyone seeing this happen might get the impression that the bird had actually been charmed.

Do Snakes Commit Suicide?

When biologists collect snakes, they sometimes jam several of the reptiles unceremoniously into a collecting bag to save space. Snakes handled in this way frequently become angry and strike blindly in all directions. Occasionally, one will bite itself instead of the object of its wrath, but usually it does not suffer any ill effects, since snakes are immune to their own poison. It has sometimes happened, however, that the teeth of the snake have penetrated its heart or another important organ, and the snake has died. Thus now and then a snake does kill itself, but whether or not this should be called suicide is difficult to say. Death by suicide is defined as death voluntarily self-inflicted, and until better methods of reading snakes' minds are developed we cannot say positively whether they kill themselves on purpose or by accident.

Do Snakes Have Legs?

In some sections of the country, it is firmly believed that all snakes have small legs, which, being deceitful creatures, they keep hidden except on special occasions. However, there is supposed to be one way in which they can be persuaded to expose their hind legs, and that is by burning them. Actually, only a few snakes have any indications of legs. Some of the boas have degenerate legs in the form of very short spurs which are on the under surface of the body near the base of the tail. The spurs are of no help in walking, but they may be of assistance during the mating process. They are visible at all times and are never withdrawn into the body.

"But," someone will exclaim, "I put a snake in the fire and saw it stick two small legs out of its body near the tail."

That person probably did see something under these circumstances, but they were not legs. All male snakes have a penis which is divided into two parts and carried within a sheath at the base of the tail. When the snake is exposed to great pain, however, such as it would experience in a fire, this double penis is frequently protruded. The untrained observer could easily mistake this divided structure for small legs.

Do Sea Serpents Exist?

Sea serpents do exist. They are not, however, the sea serpents of fable that bellow like a bull and spend most of their time hunting for a ship to attack. The true sea serpents are snakes that live along the coasts of Asia, some of the Pacific Islands, Central America and other areas. There are a number of different kinds of sea snakes, and in all of them the tail is compressed from side to side,

forming an efficient swimming organ. Most of these serpents are relatively small to medium size, being three or
four feet in length, but a few species may attain a length of
nine to twelve feet. They are related to the cobras and
are highly venomous. The venom of some species is so
potent that fish upon which they feed die almost instantly
when bitten. Yet the snakes are not aggressive and most
are loath to bite. Natives sometimes catch them accidentally
in their nets and remove them with their bare hands, but
this is a procedure that is definitely not recommended.
Many natives have died from the bites of sea serpents that
were handled too roughly and carelessly.

These real sea serpents, however, are too small to have
given rise to all the sea serpent stories that even today make
headlines in newspapers. About 1840 considerable interest
was shown in an enormous skeleton that was exhibited in
Europe as the skeleton of an authentic sea serpent. It was
114 feet long and weighed over three and a half tons. The
European tour was so successful that the owner brought
his exhibit to the United States. When the novelty wore
off and gate receipts started dropping, the man sold the
skeleton to a museum in Europe, where it was soon discovered that the skeleton was made from the bones of five
different whales.

Although no true sea serpent of the size described in the
usual story has ever been found, there are some animals
in the ocean that untrained or inebriated persons might
mistake for a sea serpent if only part of it were seen at a
distance. The oar or ribbon fish, for example, is an elongated, extremely compressed fish, believed by some to
attain a length of over fifty feet, and it has several frill-like

structures growing just behind the head. This frill could easily be taken for the "mane" of a sea serpent; for that matter, many people would assume that any fifty-foot undulating body could belong only to an enormous sea serpent. Some of the large squids, animals related to the octopus, have arms or tentacles thirty feet long, the end of each tentacle being enlarged and greatly resembling the head of a snake. Two of these tentacles writhing on the surface could also easily be taken for a sea serpent.

No sea serpent of the conventional hair-raising variety has yet been recovered, and the chances are good that none ever will be. But most open-minded biologists are willing to admit the possibility that there may be peculiar unknown creatures lurking in inaccessible parts of the ocean. One day a real flesh-and-blood sea serpent may be collected, thus confounding the skeptics.

How Many Snakes Are Poisonous?

Not nearly so many snakes are poisonous as is commonly thought. There are about 2400 different kinds of snakes known, and of this number only some 200 are dangerously poisonous to man. In most areas the number of poisonous snakes is a very small percentage of the total snake population. Australia is the one outstanding exception; there the majority of snakes are venomous.

Poisonous snakes are divided into several groups: the pit vipers, including the rattlesnakes, copperheads and water moccasins; the cobras and their relatives, the mambas and coral snakes; the true vipers, including the gaboon vipers and the various asps and vipers; and a group of snakes called sea snakes that are found in the ocean along the various coast lines.

Are Any Countries Free of Poisonous Snakes?

Venomous snakes are distributed generally over the temperate, subtropical and tropical regions of the world, but there are a few large sections that are entirely free of them. These areas include Madagascar, Ireland and New Zealand. There were no snakes of any kind in Hawaii until the recent accidental introduction of a harmless, wormlike, blind snake.

How Can You Tell a Poisonous Snake From a Nonpoisonous Snake?

The old belief that all venomous snakes have a large, triangularly shaped head and an elliptical pupil in the eye is far from correct. It is true that most pit vipers and vipers do have a large, triangular-shaped head, and most of them have an elliptical pupil, but this is also true of some nonvenomous snakes. Moreover, the head of the cobra and the coral snake is quite slender, very like the head of the racer and some other nonvenomous snakes, and the pupil is round.

There is only one relatively simple feature that invariably distinguishes a poisonous from a nonpoisonous snake, and this is a feature not easily seen unless the snake is dead. Poisonous snakes have two long teeth or fangs in the front of the upper jaw, one on each side, the rest of the teeth being much shorter. In harmless snakes, all the teeth are much the same length, none noticeably longer than the others. To examine a snake's teeth, it is, of course, necessary to open its mouth, a procedure to which a living snake will strenuously object. Great care should be taken in examining the mouth of a supposedly dead snake, since reflex muscular action may cause it to bite.

What Is the Cobra's Hood?

Many of the cobras, when angry, form what is sometimes called the hood. This is done by expanding the elongated, movable ribs which lie just behind the head. Not all cobras and their relatives are capable of forming a hood; in some, only a slight enlargement is possible; in others, none at all.

What Is the Most Poisonous Snake in the World?

Although not all venom has been analyzed, tests have shown that the venom of some snakes is, drop for drop, considerably more potent than the venom of others. The two species that are thought to have the most concentrated venom are the tiger snake of Australia and the island viper which is confined to a small island off the coast of Brazil. The tiger snake, a type of cobra, is said to be responsible for more fatalities in Australia than any other kind of snake, although the amount of venom it injects in biting is relatively small. The late Dr. Raymond Ditmars believed that it is the most venomous snake in the world. The island viper, a relative of the dreaded fer-de-lance of Central and South America, is not of particular importance because it is restricted to a single island. However, some biologists consider this the most venomous snake in the world. It feeds mostly upon birds, and a bird that is bitten dies almost instantly. Some of the sea snakes also have very powerful venoms. One species has a venom that is twice as potent, drop for drop, as that of some of the cobras.

Do Poisonous Snakes Bite or Strike?

One frequently hears that rattlesnakes and other poisonous snakes do not actually bite, but rather strike, stabbing the victim with their teeth. Actually, venomous snakes both strike and bite, but the extent of biting varies with the kind of snake. The long-fanged snakes, like the rattlesnakes and related species, do not do much chewing. When the mouth is closed, the long, hollow, movable fangs are folded inward against the roof of the mouth. In striking, the snake opens its mouth, the folded fangs fall into biting position, and the snake launches itself forward. At the moment that the fangs penetrate the skin of the victim, the snake bites. The muscles used in this biting movement press the poison glands so that the poison flows out of the poison ducts, through the hollow teeth and into the wound. The strike, the bite and the return to a coiled position are so rapid that one cannot follow the movements with the eye. Rattlesnakes and similar long-fanged serpents strike so hard that the fangs of a large specimen may penetrate even a leather boot.

Cobras and coral snakes have much shorter fangs than other poisonous snakes, and when they bite they hold on for a time and chew. The chewing movement contracts the muscles that force the poison into the wound. These snakes do not strike very hard; so rather thin canvas leggings are sufficient protection against them.

Reptiles

Can Snakes Bite Under Water?

Some people believe that snakes must strike in order to bite and that consequently they will not bite under water. If snakes were not able to bite under water a large number of water snakes would go hungry. Many of them feed upon fish and frogs, and much of the prey is captured beneath the water surface. It is thus obvious that snakes can bite under water, but it is true that, as far as man is concerned, they are not so likely to bite. The water certainly interferes with the striking power of the snake and, while a strike is not necessary for a bite, a more effective bite can be administered if the snake is free to strike.

Is a Cobra More Dangerous Than a Rattlesnake?

From the standpoint of both aggressiveness and potency of venom, cobras are considerably more dangerous than rattlesnakes.

As a rule, rattlesnakes are inoffensive and seldom attack a human being unless provoked, but the same cannot be said for some of the cobras and their relatives. Many of the cobras, mambas and related forms are quite aggressive and, during the breeding season especially, are very likely to be looking for trouble. When a rattlesnake bites, it secretes considerably more venom than does the cobra, but drop for drop the venom of the cobra is much more powerful. Elephants have been known to die as a result of a cobra bite, and in parts of India where elephants are domesticated certain trails are closed to them during the breeding season of the snakes.

People have died from the bite of a cobra in less than

an hour, but death from a rattlesnake bite usually does not occur for several hours or even a day or so.

Snakes That Spit Their Venom

One of the most striking and exasperating methods of defense that snakes have developed is found in a few cobras that actually spit or squirt their venom at their enemies. If the venom gets into the eyes it causes intense pain, and if it is not washed out, temporary or even permanent blindness may result. The venom does no damage on unbroken skin, however, and so far as is known, the eyes would not absorb enough to cause death. The snakes best known for this fiendish habit are called spitting cobras and are to be found in parts of Africa. These snakes apparently aim deliberately for the eyes and sometimes eject their venom as far as ten or twelve feet with surprising accuracy. The special structure of their fangs is responsible for their spitting ability. The poison channel in each fang turns abruptly near the outside opening. When the poison glands are compressed the venom passes down the channel, strikes the abrupt turn and squirts with considerable force from the channel opening in the front of the fang. In most poisonous snakes, the poison canal is straight, so that when venom is forced through it simply dribbles from the end of the fang.

How Many People Die From Snake Bite Each Year?

Probably more people are killed in India by snakes than in any other country. Some authorities estimate that approximately 20,000 deaths from snake bite occur in India each year, but others believe that this estimate is too high. This relatively high death rate is probably the result of the natives' habit of going barelegged and barefooted, and of the fact that in some areas snakes are not habitually killed. In the United States, it is thought that between 1500 to 1800 people are bitten each year. Of reported cases, only about five per cent are fatal, so that about 100 snakebite deaths annually would be a fair estimate for the United States.

How Does the Mongoose Kill Snakes?

Of all slayers of poisonous snakes, none is more famous than the mongoose, and fights between these creatures and cobras have become traditional. The plural of mongoose, incidentally, is mongooses, and not mongeese. It is commonly said that the mongoose is not immune to snake poison and will die if it is bitten in a fight with a cobra. However, it is now known that some kinds of mongooses are at least partly immune to cobra venom. Clifford Pope of the Chicago Natural History Museum, states that in a fight he observed the mongoose was bitten several times about the mouth and did not suffer any ill effects, although it was careful not to let the cobra bite it on other parts of the body. The poison is probably absorbed so slowly from the mouth region that no harm results. Pope believes that a mongoose might be killed if it were bitten on the body or leg.

The strike of a cobra is so slow that the agile mongoose dodges it easily or at least is able to prevent the cobra from biting it except about the mouth. Consequently, the mongoose is usually the victor, but the supposedly invincible mongoose cannot boast of such a good record in its fights with other venomous snakes. Some time ago, I heard a very interesting lecture by Dr. William Mann, Director of the National Zoological Park. He said that an attempt was once made to film a fight betwen a mongoose and a bushmaster, the dreaded pit viper of Central and South America. A bushmaster strikes more rapidly than a cobra, and eight mongooses were used before the picture was completed.

Contrary to popular opinion, mongooses do not live on a diet of snakes alone, nor do they hunt snakes more assiduously than they hunt other prey, including birds, toads, lizards, rats, eggs, and a variety of similar items.

Snakes That Eat Poisonous Snakes

Several species of snakes such as king snakes, a few racers and cobras include a certain number of venomous serpents in their diet. In the United States, the king snakes are most famous for this, but they also eat a variety of other animals such as rats, mice and birds, as well as nonpoisonous snakes. A king snake kills another snake by wrapping it body about its victim and squeezing it to death. It is relatively immune to the venom of rattlesnakes, moccasins and coral snakes; in fact, it has been known to survive large doses of their venoms.

The king cobra, widely distributed in Asia and adjacent Pacific islands, probably includes a larger percentage of snakes in its diet than any other species of serpent. Like the king snake, it eats venomous as well as harmless species, but it apparently avoids the long-fanged snakes as much as possible. Though probably immune to most venoms, it seems to realize that the long fangs of some snakes could inflict a dangerous wound.

What Is the Largest Snake?

A short time ago a youngster came into my office and asked if I knew that some boa constrictors grew to be as long as a building across the street, to which he pointed. I looked at the building and saw that it was at least seventy-five feet long. I then assured my questioner that

I did not know that the boa constrictors grew this large and asked him where he received this interesting information. He said that an older boy had given him the figures and loyally maintained that his friend was an expert on snakes. He was quite disappointed when I showed him several books which stated that the true boa constrictor is not a very large snake, and that the largest known measurement for any snake was considerably less than he had thought. This story illustrates two ideas that many people have. One is that the name boa constrictor can be properly applied to all large snakes; the other—if they know that there are several large species—is that the boa constrictor is by far the largest. Another common belief is that many of the large snakes routinely grow to lengths of sixty to seventy feet.

The term boa constrictor should be applied to only one kind of snake, and reference to the following table will show that several snakes are larger. We must become

LARGE SERPENTS OF THE BOA AND PYTHON GROUP

Species	Probable Maximum Length	General Distribution & Remarks
Regal or reticulated python	33 to 35 feet	Malay peninsula, Burma, Indo-China, Philippine Islands, and adjacent regions. There is one authentic record of a snake 33 feet long.
Anaconda	25 to 28 feet	Tropical South America. There is one authentic record of an anaconda of slightly more than 25 feet.
Indian python	22 to 25 feet	India, Malay Peninsula, adjacent regions.
African rock python	20 to 25 feet	Africa.
Diamond python	20 to 21 feet	Australia and New Guinea.
Boa constrictor	13 to 16 feet	Southern Mexico, Central and South America.

Reptiles

Species	Probable Maximum Length	General Distribution & Remarks
King cobra	18 to 19 feet	China, India, Malay Archipelago, Philippine Islands and adjacent areas. The largest verified record for this species is 18 feet 4 inches. The head of this specimen is in the Museum of Comparative Zoology at Harvard.
Bushmaster	11 to 12 feet	From Nicaragua southward throughout tropical South America.
Giant brown snake	10 to 11 feet	Australia. Aside from the king cobra, this species is the longest venomous snake in the Old World.
Eastern diamondback rattlesnake	8 to 9 feet	Southeastern United States. Ditmars states that he has measured two which were over 8 feet in length, one being 8 feet 6 inches. Another specimen of 8 feet 9 inches is on record.
Black chicken snake; pilot black snake	8 to 9 feet	Eastern United States. One authentic measurement of 8 feet 5 inches has been made.
Bull snake	8 to 9 feet	Middle United States. There is one record of a bull snake that was 7 feet 8 inches.
Indigo or gopher snake	8 to 9 feet	Southeastern United States. The largest authentic record is 7 feet 9 inches.

[213]

resigned to the fact that no living snake attains a length of sixty or seventy feet. The longest verified measurement I have seen is thirty-three feet for a regal python, and all biologists agree that snakes rarely grow even this large.

From the tables it may be noted that the regal or reticulated python is the longest snake known, although the anaconda is comparatively much heavier. Ditmars found a weight of 236 pounds for a nineteen-foot specimen, while A. Hyatt Verrill gives 360 pounds for one slightly longer. A twenty-eight-foot reticulated python exhibited by Hagenbeck weighed only 250 pounds, while another just over twenty-seven feet weighed 191 pounds.

The king cobra, with no close competitors, is the longest venomous snake in the world. There is one authentic measurement of eighteen feet four inches, while another specimen over nineteen feet long has been reported. The eastern diamondback rattlesnake of the United States has the distinction of being the heaviest poisonous snake in the world. It is very heavy-bodied as contrasted to the slender king cobra.

The probable maximum lengths of the most common larger snakes are indicated in the accompanying tables.

Do Big Snakes Eat Human Beings?

All who have investigated this matter agree that the big snakes do not attack human beings as frequently as they are reported to; nevertheless, it seems well established that a few such attacks have occurred. Several writers cite cases which they are convinced are authentic. In one instance in the East Indies, a boy of fourteen was swallowed by a python. The snake was discovered a short time later, killed, and the boy's body extracted. The size of the snake is not mentioned. Another incident occurred on the island of Ukerawe in Lake Victoria, Africa. Here, according to the story, a woman was killed by a python that measured only slightly over fourteen feet. The snake was discovered

coiled about the woman's body and was killed before it had had a chance to try to swallow it, although it is most improbable that such a small snake could have swallowed an adult human being.

One instance is of particular interest, since Frank Buck, an experienced person, was at hand when it occurred. The headsman of a tribe in the Philippine Islands kept in a cage a twenty-five-foot python which was looked upon with reverence by the natives. One day the snake escaped and, when it was found, there was a large bulge in its body, indicating that it had recently fed. Buck himself felt the outline of a human body within the snake, and several counts of the headsman's numerous children revealed that one was missing. This incident disturbed the headsman not one whit: he apparently felt that he could afford to lose additional children rather than part with his precious python. At any rate, the python was returned to its cage and allowed to digest its meal in peace.

How Big an Animal Can a Snake Swallow?

This is a subject on which the fiction writers exercise their imagination freely. And so we read with horror of the terifying experiences of some explorer who reports that several of his men have been killed and eaten by a single huge serpent, or who has seen an enormous serpent attacking and swallowing a large buffalo or crocodile. The trouble with such stories is that there are no known instances of a snake's swallowing an animal as large as a buffalo, a mature crocodile or even a lion, nor is there any evidence that snakes exist that are large enough to swallow several adult human beings in succession. The largest animal that a captive snake has been known to swallow was an eighty-four-pound goat; another snake, twenty feet in length, swallowed a hog weighing eighty pounds. A wild boar reportedly weighing 130 pounds, was taken from the stomach of a python, but I do not know the size of the snake. It is believed that an animal weighing 150 to 175 pounds is about all that even the largest snake can swallow—which is certainly far less than the weight of a buffalo or of some of the other large animals supposedly eaten by these serpents.

Such feats might be possible if, as many people believe,

the snake squeezed its prey into a pulp. However, the prey is killed not by the application of bone-crushing pressure, but of pressure only strong enough to prevent breathing and to interfere with blood circulation. The victim is not crushed out of shape at all. In fact, it is not believed that snakes are capable of exerting such enormous pressure, and it is certainly not necessary for them to do so.

How Do Snakes Swallow?

Although the capacity of snakes has been considerably exaggerated, small snakes can swallow objects large enough to make a remarkable true snake story. Many of them regularly swallow prey two or three times as big around as they are themselves. The secret of how this is done lies in the loose construction of a snake's head and in the fact that the various parts can be moved independently. In eating, the snake unhinges its jaws and advances the upper and lower jaw alternately over the body of its prey. As the size and shape of the prey make it necessary, the bones of the snake's head stretch so far out of their normal positions that one wonders if snakes actually enjoy eating. After the first part of the meal gets past the rear teeth, the muscles of the throat begin to exert pressure; this, plus wiggling movements of the body, carries the food to its final destination, the stomach.

The time required for the complete process varies considerably, depending upon the size and shape of the prey. A ten-foot python has been known to swallow a seven-foot snake of the same species in the astonishingly short time of ten minutes. Large or awkwardly shaped objects may take several hours. As the food enters the mouth it is liberally lubricated by the salivary glands, but the snake does not moisten its prey with saliva before it starts to swallow it, as has sometimes been stated.

If the swallowing process takes a long time, the snake may rest between efforts. With a large object blocking its breathing passage, it would suffocate if it did not have a special way of breathing during this time. However, it can push the end of its windpipe out between the floor of its mouth and the object which is preventing the air from reaching its lungs. After breathing for a time, the snake withdraws the tube and gets down to the business of eating again. Once the food is downed, the bones of the head return to their normal position within a surprisingly short time. Occasionaly the snake yawns a few times, which helps to restore the shape of the head.

Is the Puff Adder Poisonous?

The American spreading adder has many other common names, including hog-nosed snake, puff adder, blowing viper and sand viper. The average person who is familiar with this serpent fears it more than any other snake in the United States. When it is disturbed, it puffs up its neck to twice the normal size, takes a deep breath and then expels the air with a noise that sounds like a steam engine and can be heard for some distance. Many people believe that venom is mixed with the expelled air and that the snake's breath is therefore deadly poisonous. I have even seen published statements that human beings have been killed or severely injured by this supposedly poisonous spray at a distance of twenty-five to thirty feet! If puffing and blowing does not discourage its antagonist, the snake may strike repeatedly.

Although an expanded, blowing puff adder is a fearsome sight to people who do not know its habits, it is really one of the most harmless snakes in the United States. The show it puts on is pure bluff. Not only is the puff adder nonvenomous, but it is almost impossible to persuade it to bite. Slow motion movies have shown that the snake strikes with its mouth closed, and men who have handled puff adders say that they have never been bitten, even though they have stuck a finger in the serpent's mouth.

The puff adder's bluff does not end with spreading, hissing and striking; it has one more trick in its repertory. If its show of aggressiveness does not frighten its attacker away, the snake goes to the opposite extreme and plays dead; or at least so its actions have been interpreted. It suddenly starts writhing, as though it were having convulsions; its mouth gapes, its tongue protrudes, and after considerable thrashing around it flops over on its back and remains quiet. It even allows itself to be picked up without showing any signs of life. However, it apparently has very definite ideas as to how a truly dead snake should lie, and if it is turned over on its belly it immediately flops over on its back again. This comical and highly entertaining snake frequently makes an excellent pet.

The name puff adder is also applied to another snake, a type of viper found in Africa, which is no relation of the American puff adder. It too has the ability to puff itself up, but this serpent is highly venomous.

Must Snakes Coil in Order to Strike?

It is not necessary for a snake to coil its body before striking. Some species, such as cobras, seldom coil at all, but rear up and strike in a downward direction. Even rattlesnakes and other species that have the reputation of always coiling before striking will certainly not take the time to arrange themselves carefully into a neat coil if they are surprised. These snakes can strike quite rapidly and effectively by drawing the body into an S-shaped loop and then throwing it forward.

The striking distance of most snakes is much shorter than is commonly believed. Snakes that are violently angry and excited may strike out in all directions and from almost any position, thus giving the impression that their striking distance is much greater than it really is. One half to three fourths of their body length is the striking distance of most species. The strike of a snake is not very accurate at a distance, and most of them seem to realize this, for they seldom attempt to strike at an object the maximum distance away.

Most snakes are as earthbound as the proverbial stone and do not jump from the ground when they strike. There are, however, a few species that actually can jump a short distance, although their ability has been exaggerated. The jumping viper of Mexico and Central America, a relative of the fer-de-lance, is probably the most famous of these jumping serpents. It is venomous, and attains a length of about three feet. When it strikes, it may jump and slide forward as much as two feet; and if it strikes from a log or other elevated position it can propel its body forward for three feet or so.

The Fang in the Boot Story

One of the favorite stories about poisonous snakes current in the southwest is the one about the fang embedded in a boot. According to this story, a man was killed by a large rattlesnake which bit him through his boot. Many years later, the man's son wore the same boots and died within a short time. Some enthusiasts carry on the story of death through several generations to a particularly robust descendant who recovers from his mysterious illness and discovers a rattlesnake fang embedded in one of the boots. The fang had been broken off when the rattlesnake bit through the boot to kill the original owner.

Large rattlesnakes strike so hard that their fangs may penetrate soft boots, and it is conceivable that a fang might break off and subsequently prick a person wearing the boot at a later date. It is also true that venom retains its lethal power for a long time even though it is dried. However, it is inconceivable that a human being would die as a result of having his skin pricked by a disconnected fang. The amount of venom in a broken fang would be relatively small, considerably less than the amount required to kill a man. A person so injured would suffer at the most a slight illness—but so far I have found no verified instance of anyone's being injured that way.

Will Snakes Cross a Horsehair Rope?

A horsehair rope is frequently supposed to be a complete protection against snakes. Men have told me that they have slept on the ground perfectly content because they had encircled their sleeping bags with a horsehair rope.

If a rope of horsehair were a sleeping man's only protection against snakes, it would not be at all surprising if he were to wake up with one as a bedfellow. Rope of any type will not discourage a snake any more than will some other object of similar size. This has been demonstrated with live snakes and horsehair ropes, the proof being good photographs of serpents halfway across the rope.

However, snakes have a tendency to avoid human beings and any object to which the human odor adheres; thus a horsehair rope or any other object that had been handled sufficiently to give it human odor would probably be avoided by most snakes.

Do Fakirs Really Charm Their Snakes?

A snake charmer or fakir at work may be interesting to watch, but he does not actually charm the snakes, and many of his actions are for the benefit of his audience rather than the snakes. The eerie squeaky music he produces is a total loss as far as the snakes are concerned, for they are stone deaf. They are, however, very sensitive to any vibrations which pass through the ground or the basket in which they are kept. By surreptitiously tapping the basket or stamping on the ground, supposedly keeping time to the music, the fakir can induce the snakes to rear. As he plays his instrument, he keeps his body in constant motion, and the "dancing" or swaying of the snakes is the result of his movements. A cobra whose body is raised in striking position follows the object of its attention; as the fakir moves about, the snake also moves its body to keep its eyes continuously fixed upon the snake charmer.

What Is the Jointed Snake?

One of the most vivid impressions of my childhood is of a man vigorously lambasting what he said was a jointed snake. It seemed to me that there were at least a dozen pieces, each trying to outdo the other in the vigor with which it wiggled. The poor man seemed almost surrounded by writhing pieces of snake, and he became almost frantic trying to decide which piece he should beat. He at last compromised by beating each piece in turn until he had succeeded in drubbing them all into unrecognizable masses. Two things about this incident impressed me greatly. One was the liveliness with which the pieces of the snake wriggled, and the other was the great fear with which the man regarded it. It is small wonder that many children grow up with a deep fear of jointed snakes.

According to the usual jointed snake story, this fabulous reptile can break its body into several pieces when it is attacked. These pieces will later assemble at a previously determined place where they reunite to form again a complete snake. The only sure way to kill this dangerous creature, so the story goes, is to bury each piece separately. The snake is, of course, supposed to be deadly poisonous.

Several things are wrong with this story. The jointed snake is not a snake at all, but a legless lizard. However, it is so snakelike that people are to some extent justified in mistaking it for one. The body does not break into pieces, but the slender tail may be broken by a light blow, and the tail may break again. These detached pieces do wriggle about in quite lively fashion. While the attacker is busy subduing or beating the fiercely struggling tail into submission, the front and most important part of the lizard escapes safely into the bushes. The lizard eventually grows a new but shorter tail. The pieces of the tail that have broken off never reunite, and if the body of the lizard is injured it dies.

There are several species of jointed or glass-snake lizards in various parts of the world, but only one in the United States. These reptiles are definitely not venomous and, even if the species in this country were to bite, it could give only a slight nip. Some specimens, after they have been in captivity for a while, become quite tame, and frequently develop into interesting pets.

Snakes and legless lizards can usually be easily distinguished. A legless lizard has movable eyelids, and just behind the eye there is a rather large hole, the opening into the ear. Snakes do not have either eyelids or ear openings.

Are Brightly Colored Lizards Poisonous?

In some parts of the United States the brilliantly colored lizards have the reputation of being deadly venomous. This is especially true of the blue-tailed skinks, some of which develop a brilliant red head. These lizards, as well as other brightly colored ones, are called scorpions, and children are taught to fear them. Although some of these highly colored lizards might bite if they were caught with the naked hands, none of them are poisonous. There are almost 3000 different kinds of lizards known, and of this number only two—neither of them brilliantly colored— are venomous: the gila monster and one of its relatives, the Mexican poisonous lizard. These lizards are black with orange or yellow splotches and attain a length of about two feet. Their pebbly scales and their coloring have earned them the popular name of beaded lizards. The gila monster is found in the southwestern United States and into Mexico, its relative in Mexico and Central America.

A number of cases in which death was caused by the bite of a gila monster have been reported, but I have not found any that were positively verified. However, the gila monster is definitely venomous. There is for instance the case of a woman at the Paris Museum who was working with one of these lizards when it bit her on the finger. The wound shortly became painful, the finger swelled noticeably, and the woman suffered considerable pain, becoming faint, and developing a tendency to go into convulsions. She was quite sick for several days, and it was fully a week before she was able to return to work.

Do Chameleons Match Their Background?

Although the creature most often associated with quick color change in the mind of the average person is the chameleon, there are lizards that can do almost as well. The best known of these lizards are the American chameleons or Carolina anoles, frequently sold as true chameleons at circuses and carnivals.

That several species can make an incredibly rapid color change is quite true, but that the creatures always assume the color of their background is not true. Carefully controlled experiments have been conducted on this subject, and it has been found that the most important factors influencing color change are light, temperature, and the emotions and health of the reptile. The color of the background does not have any real effect. Thus, a Carolina anole placed upon a green leaf may turn a drab brown; if moved to a dark background, it is as likely to change to a glaring green as to keep the darker hue. It is of course true that they do often match the color of their background, but this is quite accidental. The story of the man who claimed to have driven a chameleon insane by placing it upon a plaid background must therefore be looked upon with suspicion.

Can Horned Toads Squirt Blood From Their Eyes?

One of the most interesting little creatures of the southwestern part of the United States is the so-called horned toad. A more correct name for these reptiles is horned lizards, since they are not toads at all, but true lizards. Perhaps the most improbable story connected with the horned lizards is that they squirt blood from their eyes when they become excited or angry; yet it is true. I had one of these little reptiles in a jar one day when a student who was interested in reptiles came into the laboratory. He answered affirmatively when I asked him if he wanted the lizard for his collection. As I turned back to my work, he reached into the jar to get it, and almost immediately let out a surprised shout.

"Hey, look what happened!"

I looked, to find him grinning from ear to ear, holding the lizard with one hand, and pointing to his red-spattered shirt front with the other. To this student, the soiling of a white shirt was a small price to pay for seeing a horned lizard squirt blood from the corners of its eyes. I immediately collected some of the discharged material, and an examination under a microscope showed that it was unquestionably blood.

This occurrence is thought to be the result of a rise in blood pressure which may take place during fright or anger, and which causes the capillaries near the corners of the eye socket to rupture, squirting blood for some distance.

Lizards That Fly

In the Dutch East Indies, the Malay Archipelago and adjacent areas there are several species of brilliantly colored lizards to which the name of flying dragons has been applied, although they do not look particularly like dragons. As a matter of fact, with their bright spots or splotches of red, yellow and black, which are especially noticeable when the lizards are in the air, they greatly resemble gigantic butterflies, and are sometimes called butterfly lizards. Although they are able to glide through the air for some distance, they do not actually fly. Their "wings" are folds of loose skin which are attached to and supported by movable ribs, five on each side. When the little creatures are scurrying about on the ground looking for insects, the ribs are kept folded against the body, but when one of them decides to extend its hunting grounds to a nearby tree it spreads its wings and launches itself into the air. The wings do not move, but are kept rigid, so that the lizard actually glides or sails rather than flies. The lizard's confidence in this method of travel is well founded, for it may glide safely across a space of 60 feet or even more. Despite their name, these lizards are harmless and relatively small. Their length varies from about eight to twelve inches, which includes the long slender tail.

Dragons Do Exist

About thirty years ago, the civilized world was startled by reports of the discovery of enormous man-eating lizards on some of the islands of the Dutch East Indies. Immediately the Sunday supplements of various newspapers ran accounts of many supposedly firsthand experiences, some of which told of men who had been killed and eaten by the ferocious monsters, and even described the way that steam and vapor issued from their mouths as they breathed. Biologists at that time accepted the existence of these gigantic lizards and even thought that they attained a length of over twenty feet. Because the lizards had been discovered on the island of Komodo, and because they were large and allegedly ferocious, they were called dragons of Komodo.

It is now known that many of these first stories were pure fiction. Smoke and steam of course do not issue from the lizards' mouths, and their maximum size is between ten and twelve feet rather than twenty. Several years ago I saw on exhibition a dragon of Komodo that was ten feet two inches long and weighed 365 pounds; these are the greatest actual measurements for one of the creatures of which I have any knowledge. The dragons of Komodo, however, are by far the largest of the lizards. A few other species are almost as long, but no other species is so massively built.

Stories about their ferocious nature may also be considerably discounted. Persons who have studied the reptiles in their native haunts and who have handled them in zoological parks are unanimous in saying that they are relatively mild or even timid unless cornered. A Lady Broughton went to Komodo some years ago and spent a number of days studying them, and although she was several times within a few feet of these supposedly ferocious reptiles they did not show any sign of attacking her. However, any animal of this size should be handled with caution, especially in the wild state or if newly captured. Because their natural food includes such fairly large and active animals as goats and wild pigs, they are doubtless as ferocious as they seem when in pursuit of their prey; if one were disturbed while feeding, or were brought to bay, the chances are that it would attack. The dragons of Komodo are greatly feared by the natives, but I have

never heard that one of the reptiles attacked a man unprovoked.

How to Tell an Alligator From a Crocodile

Many people, including some biologists, use the terms
alligator and crocodile indiscriminately. Actually, there
are several kinds of these creatures, all of which may be
called crocodilians, but a crocodile and an alligator are
two entirely different animals. The snout of the alligator
is very broad from the eyes out to the tip, hardly tapering
at all. The head of a crocodile has a markedly triangular
shape; the snout becomes progressively and distinctly
narrower from the eyes to the nostrils.

There are only two kinds of alligators, the American
alligator in the southeastern United States, and another in
China. Several kinds of crocodiles are to be found in
various parts of the world, but only one kind, the American crocodile, occurs in the United States and that only
in southern Florida.

Other crocodilians include the caimans and the gavials.
Caimans are limited to the western hemisphere, and
have a broad snout like an alligator. Gavials, which are
found in India and adjacent areas, are easily distinguished
by a long very thin snout, which narrows abruptly just in
front of the eyes.

Crocodilians shed their teeth frequently. The discarded
teeth are replaced by new teeth which have grown into
the hollow bases of the old ones, the old tooth not normally
being shed until the replacement tooth is quite large.

The first time I collected teeth from a crocodile's skull,
I placed them in a container and forgot about them for

several days. When I examined them later, I was surprised to see that they seemed to have increased mysteriously in number. Additional study revealed what I had not previously noticed—that well-formed smaller teeth were snugly fitted into the bases of some of the larger teeth, and some of them had become loose within the container.

Do Crocodilians Have Tongues?

Contrary to common belief, crocodilians have a well-developed tongue, but it is attached the full length of its under surface to tissues in the bottom of the mouth, so that it cannot be protruded. It can be raised, however, to prevent water from getting into the throat. By thus blocking off the throat, and by closing the valves in their ears and nostrils, crocodilians can submerge with their prey until it drowns, without themselves getting any water into the breathing passages or throat. The nostrils in all crocodilians are at the very tip of the nose, and the nasal passage opens into the throat behind the tongue. Consequently, by keeping only the end of the nose above water they can, if they wish, hold their prey under water and still continue to breathe.

Will Crocodilians Attack Human Beings?

E. A. McIlhenny, well-known naturalist, who has probably studied the American alligator more thoroughly than any other person, believes that they will attack human beings only rarely. But he describes one occasion on which he himself was the object of an unprovoked attack. He was rowing through a bayou minding his own business when suddenly a large alligator came to the surface and gave his canoe a resounding smack with its tail. The canoe upset, but the water was shallow and McIlhenny scrambled to his feet to see the alligator preparing to rush him. Fortunately he still had his gun, and a quick shot ended the alligator's desire for food. This reptile was approximately twelve feet long.

There have also been a few other supposedly well-verified reports of such attacks. It is my opinion that, although alligators usually avoid people and do not attack without good reason, they cannot be trusted entirely.

Some crocodiles, however, are confirmed man-eaters, and it has been said that probably they kill more people than any other animal except possibly the cobras. The two species with the blackest reputations are the African or Nile crocodile, and the salt water crocodile. Both these species are justly feared by the inhabitants of the areas where they are found. Not only are they a menace to those who venture into the water, but they have in numerous instances actually rushed out onto the land, seized their prey and carried it into the water to drown.

An experience related by the late Dr. Raymond Ditmars well illustrates the difference in the temperaments of alligators and crocodiles, and indicates how dangerous a crocodile can be. He once received a crated crocodilian of unspecified variety, but when it was released he saw that it was a Florida crocodile. Having had no previous experience with crocodiles, but being familiar with the reactions of alligators, he strolled up to the animal and carelessly poked it in the side with a stick. The crocodile gave an angry hiss and quick as a flash swung its tail and knocked Dr. Ditmars off his feet. Only wild scrambling saved him from serious injury, for the crocodile actually pursued him.

Lizards That Can Run on Water

Basilisks are peculiar lizards that live in South and Central America. When a basilisk wants to cover ground in a hurry, it rises on its hind legs, which are better developed than the front pair, and runs with its long trailing tail functioning as a balancing organ. As if this habit were not remarkable enough, the basilisk also has the ability to run on the surface of the water. Eyewitnesses say that it is able to run successfully across as much as a quarter of a mile of water surface. These lizards have large feet, and their bodies are not very heavy. As long as they continue to run, their speed is such that they do not sink, but if they slow up or stop, they sink as quickly as any other animal of similar size. They are good swimmers, however, and a dunking does not injure them.

Some of them grow to about three feet, but much of this length includes a very long tail. Most of them have an erectile crest on the head, and some have, in addition, finlike ridges along the back and tail. When they are angry or excited, the crest or hood is raised and the loose skin or dewlap under the lower jaw is greatly expanded.

According to mythology, a basilisk is a ferocious creature capable of killing a person with its breath or simply by looking at him. Apparently the men who first saw and named these crested lizards thought that they were comparably dangerous. The name they gave them is still used, although it is now known that they are harmless.

Some Lizards Have Three Tails!

Now and then a collector finds a lizard with as many as three tails, and a forked-tailed lizard is not too uncommon. The reason for this peculiar development is that the regenerative process by which a lizard replaces a lost tail sometimes works abnormally. When a lizard loses its tail, the injury stimulates cells within the stub to start growing, and growth continues until the tail is replaced, although the new tail, as a rule, is shorter than the original. Usually this stimulation occurs in only one part of the stub, but in some cases cells in two or more parts begin to grow independently, with two or more tails resulting. Occasionally a lizard may receive a slight injury to the tail, not sufficient to cause it to break off completely, yet sufficient to stimulate growth in the tail-producing cells. Once started, the cells continue to grow until one or more new tails have developed, although the lizard still has its original tail.

Do Crocodiles Guard Their Nests?

The female crocodilian lays from twenty to forty hard-shelled eggs in a moundlike nest of vegetation and dirt, and then covers them. Supposedly she stays in the general vicinity of the nest, occasionally—in the case of the American alligator at least—scratching around it with her wet body to keep the eggs moist. At the time of hatching, the young give vent to a series of raucous squeaks, whereupon the mother rushes to the nest, opens it, and sometimes escorts the nightmarish infants to the water and swims with them for a while. That the males of some species are not prompted by any such feeling of devotion is indicated by the report that the male South American caiman sometimes eats its own offspring if the opportunity presents itself. The female frequently comes to the rescue, fights off the male and, so the story goes, takes some of the young in her mouth and hides them in a secluded spot.

Some naturalists report that they have scratched into numerous crocodiles' nests and have never been caught in the act by an outraged female; consequently, they do not believe that any crocodilians guard their nests. Probably some species are not particularly vigilant; and in areas where the alligator has learned to fear man—and also if the female has been killed—one could probably rob the nest undisturbed. I believe, however, it has been well established that the American alligator, at least, does keep a careful watch on the nest. I also believe that female alligators help their young from the nest, and frequently swim with them for a time. However, I must have more proof before I can swallow the story that female caimans move their offspring from one place to another like a loving mother cat.

How Large Are Crocodilians?

Anyone who reads very much about crocodiles is almost certain to find record of two enormous salt water crocodiles which were reported many years ago. One of these was a thirty-three-foot crocodile which was killed in Bengal, and the other a twenty-nine-foot specimen shot in the Philippines about 100 years ago. The average crocodile or alligator was much larger many years ago than it is today. because now many more of them are killed before they attain their maximum size, but even so there is great doubt as to the accuracy of these two measurements. Fortunately—or perhaps unfortunately for the sensationalists —the skull of the reported twenty-nine-foot specimen is still in existence. Karl Schmidt of the Chicago Natural History Museum has examined it, and estimates that the crocodile would have had a maximum length of twenty-two and a half feet if it had been measured by a hard-boiled scientist. He believes that the largest crocodilian ever measured by a biologist was an Orinoco crocodile of twenty-two feet four inches, and he does not think that any grow to be over twenty-three feet. In former times, the American alligator also grew to a large size; E. A. McIlhenny reports one of nineteen feet two inches and two others of over eighteen feet. For a long time it was said that the British Museum had a mounted gavial thirty feet long, but recent investigation has revealed that this specimen had apparently mysteriously shrunk in size. The largest mounted gavial in this institution is only about fifteen feet in length.

There is certainly no argument about the fact that present-day crocodilians are mere pygmies compared with some of their extinct relatives. Those gigantic reptiles may sometimes have attained a length of fifty to sixty feet, although this exceeds estimates based upon a fossilized skull. A reconstructed skull of one of these monsters, fragments of which were discovered in the Big Bend area of western Texas, is carefully mounted in the American Museum of Natural History. It is approximately six feet in length and has teeth five to six inches long with a diameter of two inches. It has been estimated that the owner of this skull would have been over forty-five feet long, and it is quite possible that larger specimens were alive at that time.

What Are Turtles, Terrapins and Tortoises?

What is the difference between a turtle, a tortoise and a terrapin? The answer is not a simple one; even turtle experts do not agree. Most biologists use the term tortoise for those forms that live only on land and do not normally go into water. The so-called giant tortoises, which children sometimes ride in zoological parks, and the much smaller box turtles or tortoises frequently found scratching around in one's garden are thus true tortoises. The term turtle is often used for the marine species and the freshwater forms that sometimes come out of the water to bask in the sun. According to the same school of nomenclature, terrapins are those valuable hard-shelled forms, such as the diamondback, which are in demand as food. But there are many other ways that the words may be used. Fortunately, the term turtle is an acceptable one when speaking of the whole group, or when discussing some of the creatures in a general way.

Sea Turtles Are More Comfortable on Their Backs

Feminine shoppers with humanitarian ideals are some times horrified at the supposedly cruel way in which sea turtles are displayed in the fish markets: The reptiles are simply turned on their backs, and left with their flippers waving helplessly. Actually, they are far more comfortable in this position than if they were turned right side up. The under shell of the sea turtle is so weak that it is not capable of supporting the animal for any great length of time; if a turtle were to remain out of water on its stomach very long, its weight would press the lower shell upward, crushing the heart and lungs and causing death within a short time. In the natural state, this problem seldom arises, since the turtle's weight is supported by the water; they seldom venture on land except to lay their eggs.

Can a Turtle Crawl From Its Shell?

There is a widespread belief in some areas that the shell of a turtle is not attached to the reptile's body. It is thus thought that the turtle can easily come from its shell if properly persuaded. One method that has been recommended to me is placing the turtle on a hot stove.

A turtle on a hot stove would certainly crawl out of its shell if this were possible, and if by so doing the creature could escape the "hot tummy" it was getting. However, it would be just about as easy for a human being to pull off his skin and dance around in his bones as for a turtle to crawl from its shell. Part of the shell is composed of greatly flattened ribs which are fused to the remainder of the shell, and various other parts of the body such as the backbone are firmly attached to the shell. The only way a turtle can be removed from the shell is to cut him out, and even this is frequently a very difficult procedure.

Because of the shell that surrounds much of a turtle's body, the arrangement of certain body parts is different from that of other animals. One of the most interesting of these modifications is the position of the shoulder blades, the large flat bones in human beings that occur on the back just behind the arms. In animals other than turtles, these shoulder blades are outside the ribs, but in turtles the bones are inside. The attachment of the front limbs in turtles also occurs inside the ribs, a condition found in no other animal.

How Is Tortoise Shell Obtained?

Tortoise shell was at one time in great demand for making cigarette cases, snuff boxes and other trinkets, but within recent years cheaper celluloid substitutes have almost replaced the original product. True tortoise shell is obtained from a sea turtle called the tortoise shell turtle. It is also called the hawksbill, because the shape of its upper jaw greatly resembles the beak of a hawk.

Tortoise shell consists of the large transparent plates or shields that cover the bony part of the shell, and is usually obtained by the application of heat, which causes the shields to come loose from the underlying bone. One of several methods may be used, varying considerably in unpleasantness as far as the turtle is concerned. One of the cruelest methods, which has been practiced by natives in some areas, is to capture a female turtle when she comes ashore to lay eggs, bind her to a pole, lower her back downward close to a bed of embers, and leave her there until the shields peel away from the bony base. Then she is released in the hope that she will grow new plates so that she may be recaptured and repeeled. Regeneration of the plates does take place in some cases, but the new plates are usually abnormal and have little value.

While this method of peeling a living turtle doubtless shocks many readers, one possible advantage to the turtle should not be overlooked. Peeled turtles, so far as is tnown, can still reproduce, so that the practice of releasing them may have prevented their becoming extinct in many areas. In some regions, the turtles are killed and then placed in boiling water until the tortoise shell is loosened. Although this practice is more humane as far as the individual turtle is concerned, it does not contribute to the preservation of the species.

How to Catch a Sea Turtle

Because some of the sea turtles are in great demand as food, many of them are captured for the markets. In some regions, a native ties a rope about his waist, locates a turtle, attaches himself leech-fashion to its back, and hangs on for dear life while his companions haul him and his catch into the boat. If the turtle is in shallow water, the rider may wrestle it into the boat, although I have an idea that this method is used primarily for movie shorts. In some places, the turtles are harpooned or caught in nets.

Perhaps the most common practice is to take advantage of the female turtle when she comes ashore to deposit her eggs. Sometimes many of them come to the same place at the same time, so that if the "turtlers" are lucky, they may catch a large number in a single night. When the hunter locates a turtle, he turns it on its back, in which position it is helpless, then continues his search, treating all he finds in similar fashion. When he is ready, he returns and collects the catch at his leisure. Some people say that the turtle catchers allow the female turtles to deposit their eggs before capturing them; if this were the case, the practice would not be so bad. However, it is hard for me to believe that hard-boiled turtle catchers squat patiently on their haunches waiting for the female turtles to deposit their eggs when they could catch many more by collecting them at once.

Can Alligators and Turtles Mate?

Lurking in the muddy waters of the Mississippi River and other large streams of the southeastern United States are enormous turtles able and willing to take off a man's arm at a single snap. They are the largest freshwater forms in the United States, and certainly among the ugliest and most dangerous of the turtle clan. They are called alligator snapping turtles, a name which it is said was given them by the early settlers, who thought that they were the result of a cross between an alligator and a common snapping turtle. These huge sullen brutes well deserve their name but, as it happens, it is biologically impossible for alligators and snapping turtles to mate.

A 100-pound alligator snapper swimming in a clear water aquarium where all its movements can easily be watched is something to compel attention. The enormous head, the bright beady eyes, the tremendous slash of a mouth which makes the creature seem to be perpetually grinning—all these combine to inspire a feeling of awe and fear in the observer.

Can Turtles Breathe Under Water?

Most turtles cannot breathe under water, but must come to the surface for air. If their heads are held beneath the surface, they will drown just as surely as would a human being. An exception is the soft-shelled turtle which can stay under water for several hours. This is possible because just behind its mouth, in the skin of the throat, there are a large number of blood vessels which absorb oxygen from the water.

The Most Valuable Turtle in the World

The diamondback terrapins are said to be so named because the plates on their shells are diamond shaped; but in the light of what one pays for the flesh of the creatures the name is very appropriate without reference to the shell at all. The high price—which for eight-inch terrapins may range from $60.00 to $84.00 a dozen "on the hoof"—may have something to do with their popularity. It has been maintained that few people are able to distinguish between diamondback and snapping turtle when the turtles are cooked, but snapping turtle stew, so advertised, would not be nearly so popular as a dish made from the diamondback. Before the diamondbacks became so popular as food they were rather numerous along the Atlantic coast, but now, outside of terrapin "farms," they are comparatively rare. Several farms which raise diamondbacks for the market have been established in various southern states including Georgia, North and South Carolina.

Do Turtles Hibernate?

The body temperature of turtles, like the temperature of all reptiles, varies with that of the air; if they did not hibernate during cold weather they would die. Many of the aquatic and semiaquatic turtles burrow into the mud at the bottom of the body of water in which they live; land forms usually burrow into soft ground for a foot or so. During this winter sleep, they are in a stupor; they do not breathe at all unless they venture to the surface during warm spells. A hibernating turtle recovered from the bottom of a lake or stream appears to be dead, since all its body processes are slowed down. That all turtles do not successfully complete their hibernation is indicated by the number of dead turtles and shells found along the banks of lakes and streams in the spring. Many deaths are probably due to the impatience of the hibernating turtles, which, fooled by the early spring thaws into thinking that permanent warm weather has arrived, emerge prematurely from hibernation. Caught by a dropping temperature, they become stupefied with the cold and are unable to return to their hibernating quarters, and consequently die.

Do Turtles Have a Voice?

Very few turtles have a voice in the real sense of the word. Many of the reptiles hiss their displeasure by sharply expelling air from the lungs, but only a few species have definite voices. Most of the giant tortoises that live on the Galápagos and a few other islands are capable of making sounds variously described as roaring, trumpeting or bellowing. The males are prone to be especially noisy during the breeding season. Possibly these sounds, which resemble those made by a bull, are supposed to be romantic.

According to one report, there are two kinds of turtles that possess such well-developed voices that all other turtles suffer by comparison: the tabulated tortoise of the West Indies and the leopard turtle of Africa. The noise-making ability of these turtles is said to be so well developed that a group of either species can produce a hubbub which almost anyone would mistake for several yapping dogs fighting with a squealing grunting hog. But despite the novel possibilities of turtles that yap, grunt and squeal, I have not been able to confirm the presence of such a well-developed voice in any of these creatures.

The Skunk of the Turtle Family

I experienced one of the greatest shocks of my life the first time I caught a musk turtle on a fishing line. My chagrin at having landed an angry clawing turtle instead of a respectable-sized fish changed quickly to amazement and then disgust as I realized that this relatively small turtle was giving off an overpowering odor.

The musk turtles and their relatives all secrete a substance which smells to high heaven, and doubtless serves to discourage their enemies. It is a kind of yellowish liquid produced by glands which open near the edge of the upper shell. Most species are rather small, usually having a shell only four inches or less in length. They somewhat resemble small snapping turtles in that they have a pugnacious disposition and a relatively large head. If one sniff of the air ever leaves any doubt of the identity of a captive turtle the creature is not a musk turtle.

Turtles That Fish With Lures

The matamata turtle of the Amazon River and its tributaries is one of the queerest of the turtle clan. Attached to its long neck are a number of wormlike appendages, which attract the fish, frogs, and other animals upon

[244]

which it feeds; and growing on its rough irregular-shaped shell are various small water plants. When the turtle is resting on the bottom or moving slowly from one place to another, it is very difficult to distinguish from a rock or log overgrown with plant life.

The alligator snapper has a reddish filament attached to its tongue, which probably is used to attract fish. Observers have seen the turtles open their mouths and allow the wiggling "worms" to float free, although no one has ever actually seen one catch a fish this way.

How Large Do Turtles Grow?

Some of the present-day turtles are quite large, but they are all dwarfed by the size attained by several extinct species. One was a marine turtle called *Archelon* which became extinct many years ago. An almost complete skeleton of one of these gigantic creatures may be seen at the Peabody Museum of Natural History of Yale University. The shell is over twelve feet long and the skull is three feet long. It has been estimated that the living turtle weighed about 6000 pounds. Another species was a huge land tortoise that lived in India. One of the most complete skeletons of this tortoise, in the American Museum of Natural History, has a shell length of seven feet four inches over the curve, and a straight line length of five feet five inches. It is thought that this creature weighed about 2100 pounds when alive.

The largest of the turtles still in existence is the leather-back or leathery turtle, a large marine form. Most writers are agreed that the maximum weight for this species is over 1500 pounds. One specimen caught off the coast of Vancouver weighed 1450 pounds, and another taken near California weighed 1286 pounds. The total length of one of these large turtles may be as much as eight feet, and the front flippers may have a spread of eight to ten feet.

The probable maximum weight of other large species **is** indicated in the table below.

SIZE OF THE LARGEST TURTLES

Species	Probable Maximum Size	Remarks
Green turtle	800 to 900 pounds	A specimen weighing approximately 850 pounds has been caught in the West Indies. This species is the most popular of the marine turtles for use as a food.
Loggerhead	800 to 900 pounds	A turtle weighing approximately 850 pounds was caught in 1871. It had a flipper spread of 9 feet.

SIZE OF THE LARGEST TURTLES—*Continued*

Species	Probable Maximum Size	Remarks
Giant tortoises	500 to 600 pounds	One specimen in Lord Rothschild's collection in England weighed 593 pounds when alive. These tortoises occur in small numbers on Galápagos, Seychelles and Aldabra Islands.
Hawksbill	100 to 150 pounds	The smallest of the sea turtles. The species from which tortoise shell is obtained.
Alligator snapper	125 to 150 pounds	A specimen in the New York Zoological Park weighed 113½ pounds. Has been reported without confirmation to reach a weight of 200 pounds.
Common snapper	50 to 100 pounds	A weight of 87 pounds is known for one turtle that was fattened in captivity, but in nature the maximum weight is probably much less than this.

How Long Do Reptiles Live?

The most famous of the reptilian Methuselahs are the giant tortoises, although a few of the small tortoises and even crocodilians sometimes reach a ripe old age. It seems well established, however, that giant tortoises live longer than any other vertebrate animal.

The best known of the ancient tortoises include the Mauritius tortoise, brought from Seychelles to Port Louis, Mauritius, which was reported to be 130 to 200 years of age; Napoleon's tortoise, which was brought from Aldabra to St. Helena Island and was said to have been alive more than 100 years after Napoleon's death; and Captain Cook's tortoise, a giant from the Galápagos Islands, branded by the great English explorer in 1773 and left in the Tonga Islands. It is claimed that this tortoise was rediscovered in 1923, still alive but feeble; it was said to have been mentioned in a report made by the Governor of Samoa to the Navy Department of the United States.

Most biologists who have studied the matter believe that 152 years is fairly well established for the Mauritius tortoise, and that it may have lived for 200 years. Galápagos Island tortoises, including the one marked by Captain Cook, are given credit for over 100 years, and the chances are that Napoleon's friend did survive for a century or longer.

Most evidence of old age in small tortoises comes from dates carved in their shells, the worn appearance of the carving and the aged appearance of the reptiles usually lending some weight to the contention that the tortoises are in truth as old as the age indicated. Much of this evidence is probably reliable, but a carved date can easily be forged. This possibility was pointed out some time ago by a man who said that he owned a tortoise that had doubtless lived before the time of Christ, since it had the inscription "Adam I" carved in its shell. However, biologists believe that there is evidence that the Carolina tortoise of the United States may live for 123 years.

The case of an alligator snapping turtle is of particular interest. This turtle arrived at the Philadelphia Zoo in 1890, and in 1946, fifty-six years later, was still alive and in good condition. At this writing, it holds the distinction of being the oldest continuous resident of the zoo.

Crocodilians, according to tradition, are also notably long lived, and we find writers crediting the sacred crocodiles of India with from 100 to 200 years years of life. Established ages do not match this, although it is agreed that some crocodilians may well have lived longer than present records indicate. As far as authentic data are concerned, an American alligator holds the record, with a known life span of approximately fifty-six years. This reptile was in the Dresden Zoological Park, and was still alive at the time the record was made.

Selected References

In the preparation of this book, reference has been made to a large number of books, magazine articles and original scientific publications. Although it is impractical to include all the publications that have been used, the selected books (p. 251) should be of aid to readers who are interested in learning more about animals. The books in the general list consider several groups of animals, while the others are concerned primarily with the group under which they are listed. Magazines listed publish articles of general interest about animals.

SELECTED REFERENCES

General Books

Andrews, Roy Chapman, *This amazing planet*. G. P. Putnam's Sons, New York, N. Y.

Beaty, John Y., *Nature is stranger than fiction*. J. B. Lippincott Company, Philadelphia, Pa. 1941.

Berridge, W. S., *Animal curiosities*. Small, Maynard and Company, Boston, Mass. 1923.

Berridge, W. S., *Marvels of the animal world*. Small, Maynard and Company, Boston, Mass. 1922.

Boulenger, E. G., *The London zoo*. E. P. Dutton and Company. New York, N. Y. 1937.

Boulenger, E. G., *Animal mysteries*. The Macauley Company, New York, N. Y. 1927.

Buck, Frank and Weld, Carol, *Animals are like that*. Robert McBride and Company, New York, N. Y. 1939.

Clark, Austin H., *Animals of land and sea*. 2nd. ed. D. Van Nostrand Company, New York, N. Y. 1927.

Cutright, Paul Russel, *The great naturalists explore South America*. The Macmillan Company, New York, N. Y. 1940.

Ditmars, Raymond and Bridges, William, *Wild animal world*. D. Appleton-Century Company, New York, N. Y. 1937.

Evans, Bergen, *The natural history of nonsense*. Alfred A. Knopf, New York, N. Y. 1946.

Hammerton, J. A. (Editor), *Wonders of animal life*, 4 volumes. The Waverly Book Company, London, England.

Hegner, Robert W., *College zoology*. 4th ed., The Macmillan Company, New York, N. Y. 1936.

Hegner, Robert W., *Parade of the animal kingdom*. The Macmillan Company, New York, N. Y. 1935.

Hornaday, William T., *Hornaday's American natural history*. 16th rev. ed., Charles Scribner's Sons, New York, N. Y. 1935.

Hornaday, William T., *Tales from nature's wonderlands*. Charles Scribner's Sons, New York, N. Y. 1924.

Hudson, W. H., *The naturalist in La Plata*. Chapman and Hale, Ltd., London, England. 1895.

Lydekker, Richard (Editor), *Library of natural history*, 6 volumes. The Saalfield Publishing Company, New York, N. Y. 1901.

Messer, Harold Madison, *An introduction to vertebrate anatomy*. The Macmillan Company, New York, N. Y. 1942.

Animal Facts *and* Fallacies

Metchnikoff, Elie, *The prolongation of life,* English translation. G. P. Putnam's Sons, New York, N. Y. 1910.

Newman, H. H., *The phylum Chordata.* The Macmillan Company, New York, N. Y. 1939.

Osborn, Fairfield, *The pacific world.* W. W. Norton and Company, New York, N. Y. 1944.

Parker, T. Jeffery and Haswell, W. A., *A text-book of zoology,* Volume 2. Macmillan and Company, Ltd., London, England. 1940.

Protheroe, Ernest, *New illustrated natural history of the world.* Garden City Publishing Company, Garden City, N. Y.

Romer, Alfred Sherwood. *Man and the vertebrates.* University of Chicago Press, Chicago, Ill. 1941.

Shaw, Margaret and Fisher, James, *Animals as friends and how to keep them.* E. P. Dutton and Company, New York, N. Y. 1940.

Stimpson, George, *A book about a thousand things.* Harper & Brothers, New York, N. Y. 1946.

Storer, Tracy I., *General zoology.* McGraw-Hill Book Company, New York, N. Y. 1943.

Thompson, J. Arthur, *Biology for everyman,* 2 volumes. E. P. Dutton and Company, New York, N. Y. 1935.

Tressler, Donald K., *Marine products of commerce.* Reinhold Publishing Corporation, New York, N. Y. 1923.

Walls, Gordon Lynn, *The vertebrate eye.* Cranbrook Institute of Science, Bloomfield Hills, Mich. 1942.

Walter, Herbert Eugene, *Biology of the vertebrates.* rev. ed., The Macmillan Company, New York, N. Y. 1939.

Mammals

Allen, Glover M., *Extinct and vanishing mammals of the Western Hemisphere.* American Committee for International Wild Life Protection, New York Zoological Park, New York, N. Y. 1942.

Cahalane, Victor H., *Mammals of North America.* The Macmillan Company, New York, N. Y. 1947.

Carter, T. D., Hill, J. E. and Tate, G. H., *Animals of the Pacific world.* The Macmillan Company, New York, N. Y. 1944.

Dobie, J. Frank, *The longhorns.* Little, Brown and Company, New York, N. Y. 1941.

Dollman, Guy and Burlace, J. B. (Editors), *Rowland Ward's records of big game,* African and Asiatic sections. Rowland Ward Ltd., London, England. 1935.

Elton, Charles, *Voles, mice and lemmings.* Oxford University Press, Oxford, England. 1942.

Selected References

Ely, Alfred, Anthony, H. E. and Carpenter, R. R. M., *North American big game*. Charles Scribner's Sons, New York, N. Y. 1939.
Hamilton, W. J. Jr., *American Mammals*. McGraw-Hill Book Company, New York, N. Y. 1939.
Harper, Francis, *Extinct and vanishing mammals of the Old World*. American Committee for International Wild Life Protection, New York Zoological Park, New York, N. Y. 1945.
Hooton, Ernest, *Man's poor relations*. Doubleday, Doran and Company, Garden City, N. Y. 1942.
Howell, A. Brazier, *Speed in animals*. University of Chicago Press, Chicago, Ill. 1944.
Janssen, Raymond E., *The earth before man*. University of Knowledge, Incorporated, Chicago, Ill. 1938.
McSpadden, J. Walker (Managing Editor), *Animals of the world*. Garden City Publishing Company, Garden City, N. Y. 1941-42.
Mann, William M., *Wild animals in and out of the zoo*. Volume 6, Smithsonian Scientific Series, Smithsonian Institution Series, Inc., New York, N. Y. 1930.
Verrill, A. Hyatt, *Strange animals and their stories*. L. C. Page and Company, Boston, Mass. 1939.

Birds

Allen, Arthur A., *The book of bird life*. D. Van Nostrand Company, New York, N. Y. 1930.
Allen, Glover M., *Birds and their attributes*. Marshall Jones Company, New York, N. Y. 1925.
Aymar, Gordon C., *Bird flight*. Dodd, Mead and Company, New York, N. Y. 1935.
Daglish, Eric Fitch, *The life story of the birds*. William Morrow and Company, New York, N. Y. 1930.
Forbush, E. H. and May, John B., *Natural history of the birds of eastern and central North America*. Houghton Mifflin Company, Boston, Mass. 1939.
Griscom, Ludlow, *Modern Bird Study*. Harvard University Press, Cambridge, Mass. 1945.
Hausman, Leon Augustus, *The illustrated encyclopedia of American birds*. Halcyon House, New York, N. Y. 1944.
Herrick, Francis Hobert, *The American eagle*. D. Appleton-Century Company, New York, N. Y. 1934.
Herrick, Francis Hobert, *Wild birds at home*. D. Appleton-Century Company, New York, N. Y. 1935.
Lincoln, Frederick C., *The migration of American birds*. Doubleday, Doran and Company, New York, N. Y. 1939.

Animal Facts *and* Fallacies

Murphy, Robert Cushman, *Oceanic birds of South America*, 2 volumes. The American Museum of Natural History, New York, N. Y. 1938.

Pearson, T. Gilbert (Editor-in-Chief), *Birds of America*. Garden City Publishing Company, Garden City, N. Y. 1936.

Peterson, Roger Tory, *A field guide to the birds*. rev. ed., Houghton Mifflin Company, Boston, Mass. 1947.

Pycraft, W. P., *Birds of other lands*. Volume 6, Nature Lover's Library, The University Society, New York, N. Y. 1917.

Sturgis, Bertha B., *Field book of birds of the Panama Canal Zone*. G. P. Putnam's Sons, New York, N. Y. 1928.

Verrill, A. Hyatt, *Strange birds and their stories*. L. C. Page and Company, Boston, Mass. 1938.

Wetmore, Alexander, *Birds*. Volume 9, Smithsonian Scientific Series, Smithsonian Institution Series Inc., New York, N. Y. 1930.

Fish

Beebe, William, *Zaca venture*. Harcourt, Brace and Company, New York, N. Y. 1938.

Breder, Charles M., *Field book of marine fishes of the Atlantic coast*. G. P. Putnam's Sons, New York, N. Y. 1929.

Evans, H. Muir, *Sting-fish and seafarer*. Faber and Faber Ltd., London, England. 1943.

Hildebrand, S. F., *Fishes*. Volume 8, Smithsonian Scientific Series, Smithsonian Institution Series Inc., New York, N. Y. 1930.

Jordan David Starr and Evermann, Barton. *American food and game fishes*. Doubleday, Doran and Company, New York, N. Y. 1902.

Kyle, Harry M., *The biology of fishes*. The Macmillan Company, New York, N. Y. 1926.

La Monte, Francisca, *North American game fishes*. Doubleday and Company, Garden City, N. Y. 1945.

Mellen, Ida M. and Lanier, Robert J., *1001 questions answered about your aquarium*. Dodd, Mead and Company, New York, N. Y. 1935.

Nichols, John T. and Bartsch, Paul, *Fishes and shells of the Pacific world*. The Macmillan Company, New York, N. Y. 1945.

Norman, J. R., *A history of fishes*. Ernest Benn Ltd., London England. 1936.

Verrill, A. Hyatt, *Strange fish and their stories*. L. C. Page and Company, Boston, Mass. 1938.

Amphibians

Barbour, Thomas, *Reptiles and amphibians*. Houghton Mifflin Company, Boston, Mass. 1926.

Selected References

Bishop, S. C., *Handbook of salamanders.* Comstock Publishing Company, Ithaca, N. Y. 1943.

De Sola, Ralph (Editor), *Reptiles and amphibians.* Albert Whitman and Company, Chicago, Ill. 1939.

Gilmore, Charles W. and Cochran, Doris M., *Amphibians.* Volume 8, Smithsonian Scientific Series, Part 2. Smithsonian Institution Series Inc., New York, N. Y. 1930.

Noble, G. Kingsley, *The biology of the Amphibia.* McGraw-Hill Book Company, New York, N. Y. 1931.

Saiville-Kent, E., *Amphibians.* Volume 6, Nature Lover's Library, The University Society, New York, N. Y. 1917.

Wright, A. A. and Wright, Albert Hazen, *Handbook of frogs and toads.* Comstock Publishing Company, Ithaca, N. Y. 1942.

Reptiles

Berridge, W. S., *All about reptiles.* Robert McBride and Company, New York, N. Y.

Cochran, Doris M., *Poisonous reptiles of the world.* Smithsonian Institution War Background Studies, Number 10. Smithsonian Institution, Washington, D. C. 1943.

De Sola, Ralph (Editor), *Reptiles and amphibians.* Albert Whitman and Company, Chicago, Ill. 1939.

Ditmars, Raymond, *Reptiles of the world.* rev. ed., The Macmillan Company, New York, N. Y. 1933.

Ditmars, Raymond, *Snakes of the world.* The Macmillan Company, New York, N. Y. 1931.

Gadow, Hans, *Amphibia and reptiles.* Macmillan and Company, Ltd., London, England. 1901.

Gilmore, Charles and Cochran, Doris M., *Reptiles.* Volume 8, Smithsonian Scientific Series, Part 3. Smithsonian Institution Series Inc., New York, N. Y. 1930.

Loveridge, Arthur, *Reptiles of the Pacific world.* The Macmillan Company, New York, N. Y. 1945.

McIllhenny, E. A., *The alligator's life history.* The Christopher Publishing House, Boston, Mass. 1935.

Pope, Clifford H., *Turtles of the United States and Canada.* Alfred A. Knopf, New York, N. Y. 1939.

Pope, Clifford H., *Snakes alive and how they live.* Viking Press, New York, N. Y. 1930.

Pope, Clifford H., *The poisonous snakes of the New World.* New York Zoological Society, New York, N. Y. 1944.

Reese, Albert M., *The alligator and its allies.* G. P. Putnam's Sons, New York, N. Y. 1915.

Animal Facts *and* Fallacies

Saiville-Kent, W., *Reptiles*. Volume 6, Nature Lover's Library, The University Society, Inc., New York, N. Y. 1917.

Schmidt, Karl P., *The truth about snake stories*. Leaflet Number 10, Chicago Natural History Museum, Chicago, Ill. 1944.

Schmidt, Karl P. and Davis, Dwight, *Field book of snakes*. G. P. Putnam's Sons, New York, N. Y. 1941.

Smith, Hobart M., *Handbook of lizards*. Comstock Publishing Company, Ithaca, N. Y. 1946.

Verrill, A. Hyatt, *Strange reptiles and their stories*. L. C. Page Company, Boston, Mass. 1937.

Magazines

American Biology Teacher, The. Published by the National Association of Biology Teachers, Lancaster, Pa.

Animal Kingdom. Published by the New York Zoological Society, New York, N. Y.

Fauna. Published by the Zoological Society of Philadelphia, Philadelphia, Pa.

Field and Stream. Published in New York, N. Y.

National Geographic Magazine. Published by the National Geographic Society, Washington, D. C.

Natural History. Published by the American Museum of Natural History, New York, N. Y.

Nature Magazine. Published by the American Nature Association, Baltimore, Md.

School Science and Mathematics. Published by the Central Association of Science and Mathematics Teachers, Chicago, Ill.

Science Digest. Published in Chicago, Ill.

Science Illustrated. Published by McGraw-Hill Book Company, New York, N. Y.

Scientific Monthly. Published by the American Association for the Advancement of Science, Washington, D. C.

Index

Index

Index

Index

Index

Index

Index

Index

Index

Index

Index

Index